POLLEN AND SPORE MORPHOLOGY/
PLANT TAXONOMY

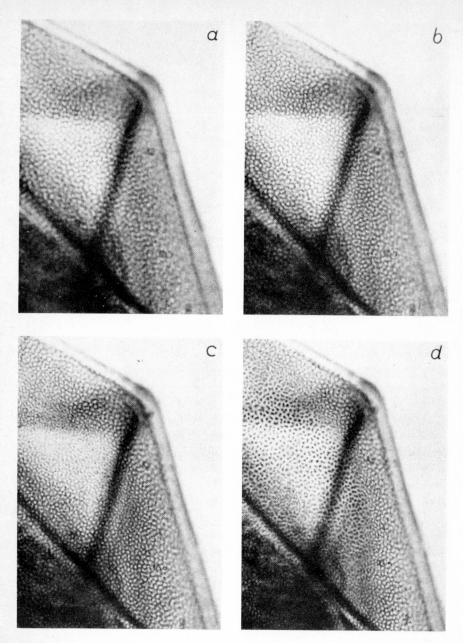

Juniperus communis, part of an acetolyzed megaspore membrane at different adjustments of the microscope from high (a) to low (d). × 1000.

POLLEN AND SPORE

MORPHOLOGY/

PLANT TAXONOMY

GYMNOSPERMAE, PTERIDOPHYTA, BRYOPHYTA

(ILLUSTRATIONS)

(An Introduction to Palynology. II)

BY

G. ERDTMAN

(Corrected Reprint of the 1957 Edition, Supplement omitted)

With Frontispiece, 5 plates and 253 illustrations

HAFNER PUBLISHING COMPANY
NEW YORK
1972

Copyright © 1957, by Gunnar Erdtman

Reprinted by arrangement, 1972

Published by

HAFNER PUBLISHING COMPANY, INC.

866 Third Avenue

New York, N.Y. 10022

Library of Congress Catalog Card Number: 66-27973

Printed in the U.S.A.

PREFACE

The second part of "An Introduction to Palynology" deals, as was originally planned, with pollen and spore morphology in the Gymnospermae, Pteridophyta, and Bryophyta. Although the illustrations and most parts of the text were ready for printing in the autumn of 1956, the completion of the text had to be somewhat postponed on account of my absence abroad for several months. It was accordingly decided to publish the second part in two instalments: thus, the present volume (Vol. II) consists mainly of illustrations, whereas the following volume (Vol. III) will provide the related text.

Most of the illustrations are palynograms drawn after the author's originals by Anna-Lisa Nilsson. They depict, in a standardized manner, a pollen grain or spore in polar and/or lateral view, together with its sporoderm stratification and other details. It should be emphasized, however, that the sporoderm stratification details merely hint at the great array of patterns and layers which exist. Pending thorough morphological investigations, the proper interpretation of these layers etc. is still, in many cases, largely conjectural.

Besides the palynograms, some photomicrographs and electron micrographs of very thin sections through spore walls are included. Stimulated by my eminent friend, Dr. R. W. Kolbe, the microscopist and diatom specialist, I tentatively took up—in the late nineteen-forties—electron microscopy as an aid in sporoderm research. These studies have been continued, with better technique and greater success, by Dr. Barbro Afzelius, to whom I am indebted for the electron micrographs here reproduced (with the exception of those of Pl. IV and V, which were put at my disposal by Professor D. von Wettstein).

In conformity with Vol. I, the present volume has been prepared under the auspices of the Swedish Natural Science Research Council. Help and support of various kinds received from other sources will be duly acknowledged in Vol. III.

Lilla Frescati, 104 05 Stockholm, June 1972   *G.E.*

CONTENTS

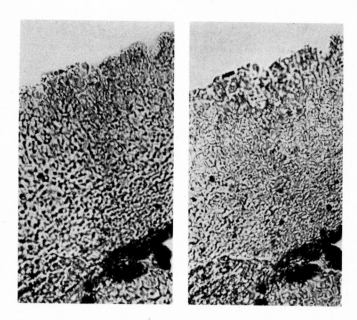

Fig. 1. *Setosisporites* sp. (material supplied by Dr. Gerhard Kremp), section (thickness about 0.5 μ) through part of the sclerine at high (left) and low (right) adjustment of the microscope. × 1000.

INTRODUCTION

ON THE EXINE MORPHOLOGY OF THE SACCATE POLLEN GRAINS IN RECENT GYMNOSPERMS

The saccate pollen grains in recent gymnosperms are heteropolar, bilateral or radiosymmetric (sometimes slightly asymmetric). They consist of a body (corpus) and a varying number of airsacks or bladders (sacci). The aperture is distal, and should often perhaps more appropriately be referred to as a tenuitas (i.e., a thin aperturoid area functioning as an aperture and gradually merging into the surrounding exine). It has earlier, as a rule, been described as a sulcus or a sulcoid groove.

The surface of the corpus of a pollen grain with n bladders can be divided into the following areas: n saccale areas, forming the floor of the sacci, n mesosaccale areas (mesosaccia), i.e. areas between the sacci and in the same latitude as these, and finally two aposaccale areas (aposaccia), one at the distal pole, and the other, usually much larger than the former, in the proximal face of the grain with the proximal pole in its centre.

With respect to the thickness of the exine of the corpus certain pollen types (cf. e.g. Figs. 53 and 57) exhibit two distinct exine areas: a proximal, crassi-exinous (referred to as cap, cappa), and a distal, tenui-exinous (referred to as cappula). The non-saccale exine of the cappa consists of comparatively thick sexine and thin nexine. The outer, ectosexinous part of the sexine is usually thin, tectoid, and as a rule connected to the nexine—except within the sacci—by baculoid, densely spaced endosexinous elements.

The sacci are separated from the interior, non-exinous parts of the corpus, by saccale nexine. Their outer wall consists of thin ectosexine which is often perforated (shown in electron micrographs—not published—by Erdtman and Thorsson in 1949). The small holes (nanopuncta) are usually difficult to observe through an ordinary light microscope. In the majority of the *Tsuga* species the ectosexine of the sacci (as well as that of the corpus, cf. Fig. 73) is studded with spinules or small spines. Attached to the inner surface of the outer wall of the sacci are endo-sexinous elements protruding into the lumen of the bladders (in *Pherosphaera fitzgeraldii* stray endosexinous rods are also found on the saccale nexine). These elements are more widely spaced than those of the body. Branched or unbranched, single or combined in different ways, they tend to produce an array of patterns which are difficult to draw and hard to describe. Microtome sections (cf particularly Afzelius in Grana palynologica, 1:2, 1956) make these subtle details of pollen construction easier to observe and safer to interpret.

Near the proximal root of the sacci are often found slight, sexinous ridges or frill-like projections (proximal crests, cristae proximales, also referred to as cristae marginales) varying in appearance in different species. At the distal root of the sacci, where these merge into the distal aposaccium, the characteristic pattern of the bladders comes abruptly to an end.

The height of the corpus coincides with the polar axis (i.e. the perpendicular line connecting the poles); the breadth is identical with its maximum horizontal extension in grains in equatorial longitudinal view (marginal crests extending beyond the general surface of the corpus not included), and the depth (in bilateral grains) is equal to the transverse ("non-sacciferous") diameter of the corpus. It is often preferable and, at the same time, easier to calculate the inner dimensions of the corpus.

The height of a saccus is the shortest distance from the highest point of the saccus (or from a line drawn through this point parallel to the saccale nexine) to the underlying nexine of the corpus. Its breadth is equivalent to the "tangential" diameter of the saccus in pollen grains in polar view. In radiosymmetric grains the breadth can also be measured in pollen grains seen in equatorial view; bilateral grains must be in a transverse equatorial position if the breadth shall be measured. In microscope slides this, however, is seldom the case. Its depth—in bilateral grains—is equal to the maximum diameter of the saccus in grains in equatorial longitudinal view. In radiosymmetric grains the depth is calculated is a similar way. Height, breadth, and depth of corpus and sacci are illustrated in Figs. 2, 3, 13, 23, 27, 43, 53, 57, 58, and 62.

As shown by Afzelius the inner part of the nexine (nexine-2) in *Cedrus* is laminated (Fig. 12, p. 11). In acetolyzed pollen grains of this genus, and of *Abies*, etc., it can often be seen, even by means of an ordinary microscope, that the nexine consists of two distinct layers, which often split apart as a result of the chemical treatment. So striking is this feature that it seems extraordinary that it has not been mentioned until now.

The morphology of disaccate pollen grains has been dealt with by numerous botanists, among whom was Strasburger, who believed that the floor of the sacci was formed by intine. This opinion has often been echoed right up to recent years, although Strasburger himself soon corrected his mistake.

In conclusion, it ought to be mentioned that, according to Čiguriaeva, the thin ends (with sexine and nexine slightly separate from each other) of the pollen grains in *Ephedra* and *Welwitschia* may be interpreted as the remainder of true sacci.

GYMNOSPERMAE

Frontispiece; Pl. I (facing p. 12), Pl. II (facing p. 20); Figs. 2–73.

MEGASPORES

Cupressaceae: Frontispiece; Figs. 36–41 (pp. 23–25).

Pinaceae: Figs. 44 (p. 28), 52 (p. 32), 63 d (p. 40).

Podocarpaceae: Fig. 19 (p. 14).

POLLEN GRAINS

Araucariaceae: Figs. 5 (p. 8), 7 (p. 9).

Cephalotaxaceae: Pl. I (Fig. 2); Fig. 14 (p. 12).

Cupressaceae: Figs. 4 (p. 8), 11 (p. 10), 29 (p. 18), 42 (p. 26), 49 (p. 30), 54 (p. 34), 71 (p. 43).

Cycadaceae: Figs. 10 (p. 10), 17 (p. 13), 18 (p. 13), 28 (p. 18), 31 B (p. 20), 46 (p. 29), 67 (p. 42).

Ephedraceae: Pl. II; Figs. 30 A, B (p. 19), 31 A (p. 20).

Ginkgoaceae: Fig. 32 (p. 21).

Gnetaceae: Figs. 34, 35 (p. 22).

Pinaceae: Figs. 2 (p. 6), 12, 13 (p. 11), 43 (p. 27), 45 (p. 28), 53 (p. 33), 55–58 (pp. 34–36), 62 (p. 39), 63 a–c (p. 40), 73 (p. 44).

Podocarpaceae: Figs. 3 (p. 7), 20-27 (pp. 14-18), 48 (p. 30), 51 (p. 31), 59-61 (pp. 37, 38), 64 (p. 40).

Taxaceae: Figs. 6 (p. 8), 9 (p. 9), 50 (p. 31), 70 (p. 42).

Taxodiaceae: Figs. 8 (p. 9), 15 (p. 12), 16 (p. 12), 33 (p. 21), 47 (p. 29), 65, 66 (p. 41), 68, 69 (p. 42), 72 (p. 43).

Welwitschiaceae: Fig. 30 C (p. 19).

ABIES:—

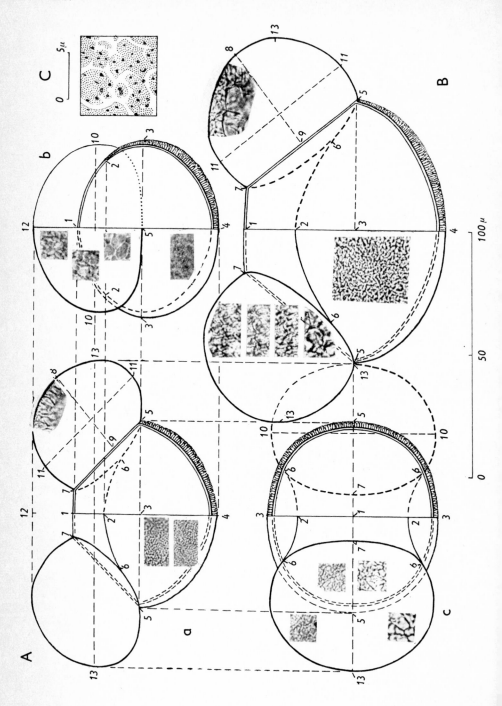

Fig. 2. A, *Abies nephrolepis*; a, lateral longitudinal view; b, lateral transverse view; c, polar view (distal face). × 650. B, *A. magnifica*, lateral longitudinal view. × 650. C, *A. mariesii*, saccus pattern (about × 2500).

1: distal pole, 4: proximal pole. Corpus: height 1–4, breadth 5–5, depth 3–3. Sacci: height 9–8, breadth 10–10, depth 11–11. Total grain: height 4–12 (A: a, b), breadth 13–13, depth 3–5–3 (A: b), 3–2–1–2–3 (A: c). Eleven of the inserted photomicrographs show the pattern of the outer surface of the sacci at different foci (the uppermost photomicrograph in each saccus shows the pattern at high adjustment of the microscope, the lowermost the same at low adjustment). Two of the photomicrographs between numerals 11 and 8 in A: a and B show a part of the saccus in optical cross-section. The remaining four photomicrographs exhibit the pattern of the corpus. Those in A: b are phase contrast pictures. (From Erdtman in Svensk bot. Tidskr. 1954.)

ACMOPYLE:—

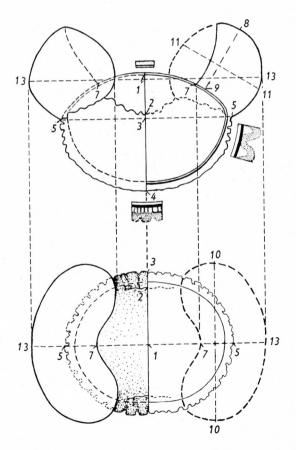

Fig. 3. *Acmopyle pancheri*. For explanation of numerals see Fig. 2.

8

ACTINOSTROBUS:—

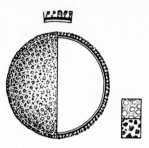

Fig. 4. *Actinostrobus acuminatus,* surface and optical cross-section. ×1000.

AGATHIS:—

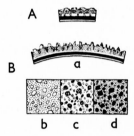

Fig. 5. A, *Agathis microstachya,* exine stratification. × 2000. B, *A. ovata,*
exine stratification (a; × 2000) and LO-patterns (b–d).

AMENTOTAXUS:—

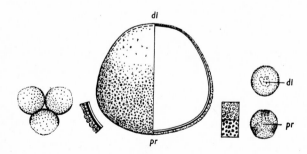

Fig. 6. *Amentotaxus argotaenia;* di, distal pole; pr, proximal pole. From left
to right: three still loosely united pollen grains (tenuitas distal; × 250); exine
stratification (× 2000); lateral view, surface and optical cross-section (×1000);
LO-patterns; pollen grains in polar view (× 250).

ARAUCARIA:—

Fig. 7. *Araucaria montana* (exine stratification). a, transition from tenuitas (left) to the thickwalled rest of the grain (right). Layers interpreted in the same way as in b. — b and c, exine stratification outside tenuitas (alternative interpretations); c, shows a thin "nexine" (possibly consisting of two layers) overlain with a thick "sexine" exhibiting three layers: an "endosexinous" faintly-marked layer (consisting of baculoid rods?) merging into a thick, ± granular "ectosexine" ("tectum"), beset with piloid "supratectal" processes. According to the interpretation given in b, thin "sexine" ("pila") covers a thick "nexine" (the rest of the exine). — d, LO-patterns ("pila"). × 2000.

ARCEUTHOS: see Fig. 42 B, p. 26.

ATHROTAXIS:—

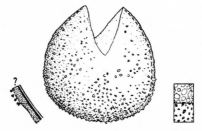

Fig. 8. *Athrotaxis cupressoides*. From left to right: exine stratification (×2000); lateral view of opened grain (× 1000); LO-patterns.

AUSTROTAXUS:—

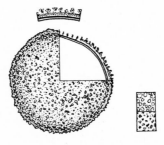

Fig. 9. *Austrotaxus spicata*. Main figure: surface and optical cross-section (× 1000). Details: exine stratification (× 2000) and LO-patterns.

BOWENIA:—

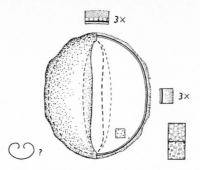

Fig. 10. *Bowenia spectabilis*. Details marked 3 × enlarged 3000 times. The main figure shows the distal face (surface and optical cross-section). × 1000.

CALLITRIS:—

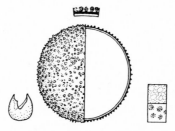

Fig. 11. *Callitris balansae* var. *alpina*. Main figure: surface and optical cross-section (× 1000). Details (from left to right): lateral view of opened grain (× 250); exine stratification (× 2000); LO-patterns.

CEDRUS:—

C. atlantica [Pl. I (facing p. 12); Fig. 12 a, b], *C. deodara* (Fig. 13).

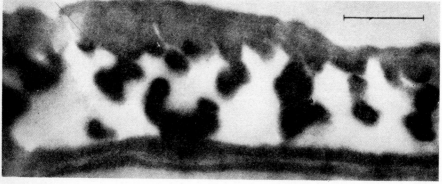

a

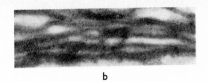

b

Fig. 12. *Cedrus atlantica.* a, section through part of an acetolyzed pollen wall; from top to bottom: ectosexine, endosexinous rods, nexine-1 (homogeneous), nexine-2 (laminated; the black horizontal line indicates 1 μ; × 22.000); b, nexine-2 (from another section; magnification greater than in a). EMG B. M. Afzelius.

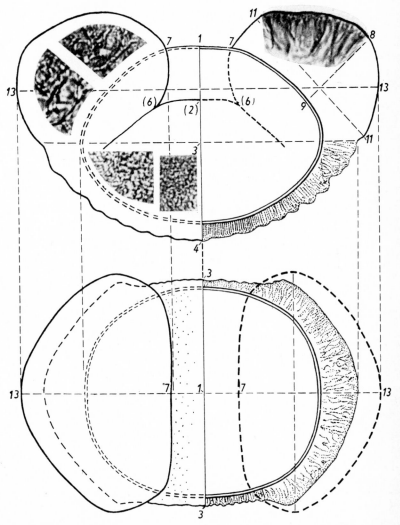

Fig. 13. *Cedrus deodara.* For explanation of numerals see Fig. 2, p. 7.

CEPHALOTAXUS:—

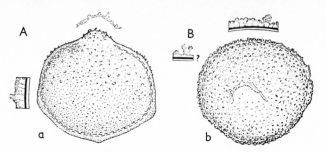

A B

a b

Fig. 14. A, *Cephalotaxus drupacea*; a, pollen grain with evaginated tenuitas (lateral view, × 1000); b, pollen grain with invaginated tenuitas (distal face, × 1000). B, *C. nana*, exine stratification (× 2000). — The drawings for this figure were ready before the electron micrograph, Pl. I, Fig. 2, was taken. The white counterpart ("nexine-2") to the lamellar layer in the EMG is clearly seen. Superimposed on the "nexine-2" is a black layer ("ecto-nexine") corresponding, it would seem, to the granular part of the "nexine" shown in the EMG. Also with regard to sexine details there is an obvious similarity between Fig. 14 and the EMG, Pl. I, Fig. 2.

CHAMAECYPARIS:—

Megaspore membrane: *Chamaecyparis lawsoniana*, see Fig. 36, p. 23.
Pollen grains: *Chamaecyparis pisifera*, see Fig. 42 A, p. 26.

CRYPTOMERIA:—

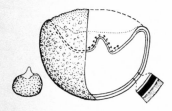

Fig. 15. *Cryptomeria japonica*. From left to right: pollen grain in lateral view, surface (× 250); pollen grain (distal face invaginated) in lateral view, surface and optical section (× 1000); exine stratification (× 2000).

CUNNINGHAMIA:—

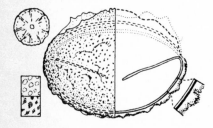

Fig. 16. *Cunninghamia lanceolata*. From left to right: distal face (upper detail-figure; × 250), LO-patterns (lower detail-figure); lateral view, surface and optical section (distal face invaginated; × 1000); exine stratification (× 2000).

Pl. I.

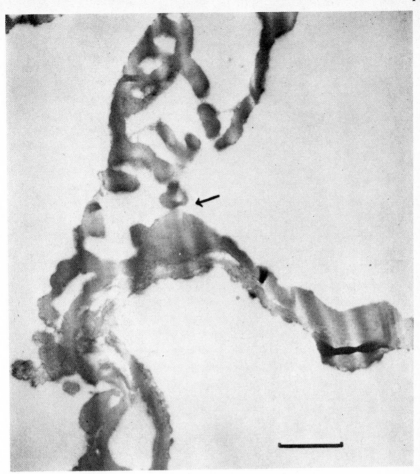

Fig. 1. *Cedrus atlantica*, section through part of an acetolyzed pollen wall. The nexine has been split off from the sexine at the point indicated by the arrow. The nexine-2 is laminated. × 18,000. The black horizontal line indicates 1 μ. (EMG; from Afzelius, in Grana palynologica, 1: 2, 1956.)

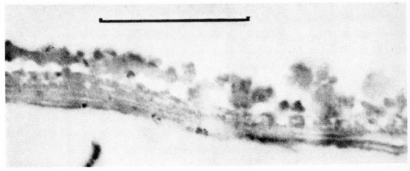

Fig. 2. *Cephalotaxus nana*, exine stratification. × 42,000. The black horizontal line indicates 1 μ. (EMG; from Afzelius, in Grana palynologica, 1: 2, 1956.)

CUPRESSUS: —

Megaspore membrane: *Cupressus arizonica*, see Fig. 37, p. 23; *C. whitleyana*, see Fig. 38, p. 24.

CYCAS (see also Fig. 31 B, p. 20):—

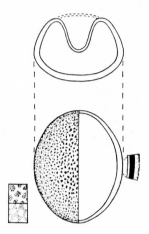

Fig. 17. *Cycas revoluta*; outline of transverse median section (upper detail-figure); proximal face (lower detail-figure).

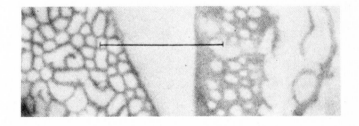

Fig. 18. *Cycas revoluta*, sections through part of acetolyzed pollen walls: cf. tangential, ± oblique section (left); ± radial section (right; × 34,000). The black horizontal line indicates 1 μ. EMG B. M. Afzelius.

DACRYDIUM:—

Megaspore membrane: *D. cupressinum* (Fig. 19).

Pollen grains: *D. araucarioides* (Fig. 20 B), *D. bidwillii* (Fig. 21), *D. elatum* (Fig. 20 A), *D. falciforme* (Fig. 22), *D. fonkii* (Fig. 23), *D. franklinii* (Fig. 24), *D. guillauminii* (Figs. 25 and 26), *D. taxoides* (Fig. 27).

Fig. 19. *Dacrydium cupressinum*; megaspore membrane (× 2000) and LO-patterns of same.

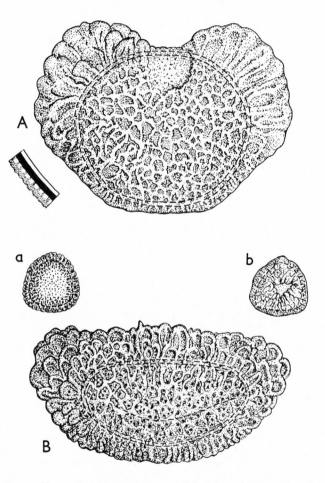

Fig. 20. A, *Dacrydium elatum*; exine stratification in proximal aposaccium (× 2000) and pollen grain in lateral, longitudinal view (surface; nexine contours indicated by broken lines; × 1000). B, *D. araucarioides*; pollen grain in lateral, longitudinal view (surface; distal face invaginated as indicated by the broken line just below the centre of the figure; × 1000); a, proximal face (× 250); b, distal face (× 250).

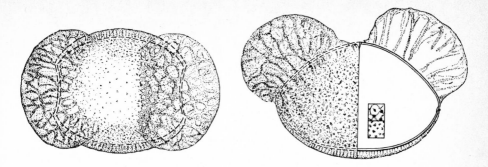

Fig. 21. *Dacrydium bidwillii*; distal face (left) and pollen grain in lateral, longitudinal view (surface, optical section, and LO-patterns). × 1000.

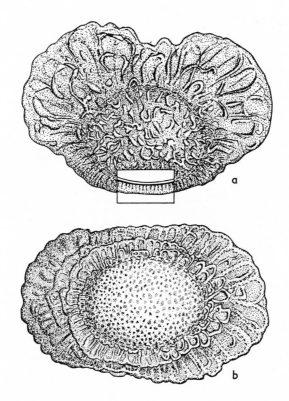

Fig. 22. *Dacrydium falciforme*; a, lateral view; b, proximal face. × 1000.

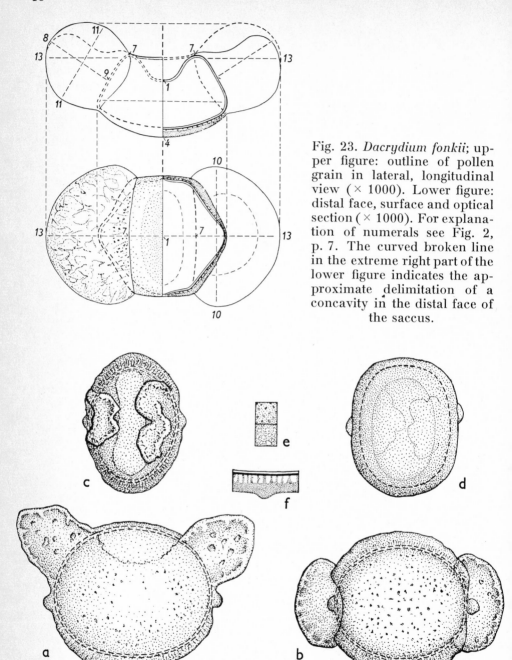

Fig. 23. *Dacrydium fonkii*; upper figure: outline of pollen grain in lateral, longitudinal view (× 1000). Lower figure: distal face, surface and optical section (× 1000). For explanation of numerals see Fig. 2, p. 7. The curved broken line in the extreme right part of the lower figure indicates the approximate delimitation of a concavity in the distal face of the saccus.

Fig. 24. *Dacrydium franklinii*; a, lateral, longitudinal view; b, proximal face; c–d, ± deviating grains (c distal, d proximal face); e, LO-patterns; f, exine stratification, proximal face (× 2000; a–d × 1000).

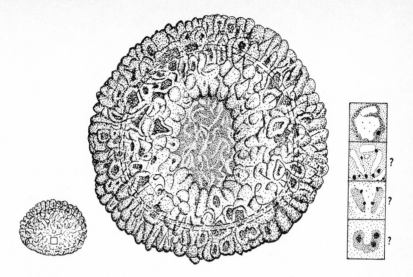

Fig. 25. *Dacrydium guillauminii*. From left to right: lateral view (× 250); distal face (× 1000); LO-patterns at high and successively lower focus.

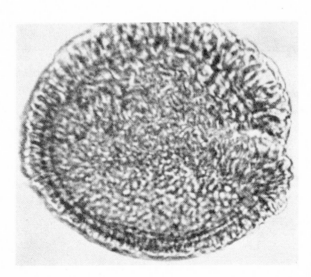

Fig. 26. *Dacrydium guillauminii*; oblique view (slightly > × 1000).

18

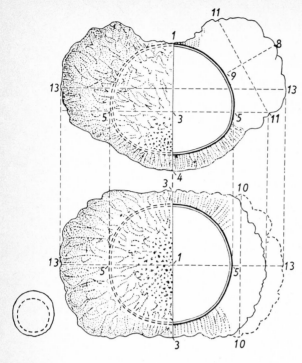

Fig. 27. *Dacrydium taxoides.*
Upper figure: pollen grain
in lateral, longitudinal view,
surface and section. Lower
figure: proximal face, surface (left) and optical section (right; × 1000). Lower
left-hand detail-figure: outline of pollen grain in lateral,
transverse view (× 250; outer
contour of the corpus marked by the broken line).
For explanation of numerals
see Fig. 2, p. 7.

DIOON:—

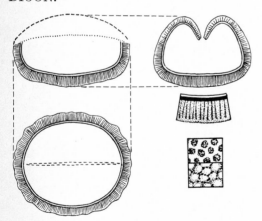

Fig. 28. *Dioon edule*; upper left-
hand detail figure: median sagit-
tal section; lower left-hand detail-
figure: frontal section; upper right-
hand detail-figure: transverse section (all × 1000); lower right-
hand detail-figures: exine stratification (× 1000) and LO-patterns.

DISELMA:—

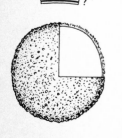

Fig. 29. *Diselma archeri*; surface and optical section (× 1000); exine stratification (× 2000); LO-
patterns.

EPHEDRA [Fig. 30 A, B, Fig. 31 A, Pl. II (facing p. 20)], WELWITSCHIA (Fig. 30 C): —

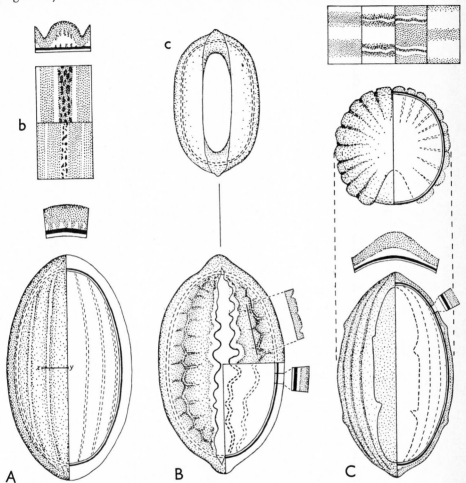

Fig. 30. A, *Ephedra antisyphilitica*; uppermost detail-figure: section through the exine along line x–y in the main figure (× 2000); b, LO-patterns; the detail-figure (× 2000) between this figure and the main figure (× 1000) shows a section through the exine at one of the short ends. B, *E. equisetina*; cf. distal face (× 1000), surface and optical section; c, young grain with sulcoid aperture. C, *Welwitschia mirabilis*; cf. lateral, transverse view (× 1000), exine stratification (× 2000), and cf. distal face (× 1000); uppermost detail-figure: LO-analysis of part of the exine surface (to be read from left to right); as the two central details show there is a very low and narrow ridge (bright in the second, dark in the third detail from the left) at the bottom of the valleys (stippled in the extreme left, white in the extreme right detail) separating the hollow sexine ridges (white in the extreme left, stippled in the extreme right detail).

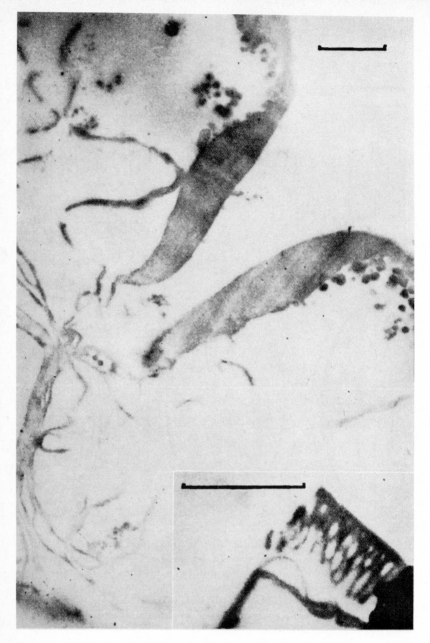

Fig. 31. A (main figure): *Ephedra monosperma*; section through an acetolyzed pollen wall. × 19,000. B (lower right-hand corner): *Cycas revoluta*; section through part of an acetolyzed pollen wall. × 35,000. The black horizontal lines indicate 1 μ. (EMG; from Afzelius in Grana palynologica, 1:2, 1956.)

Pl. II.

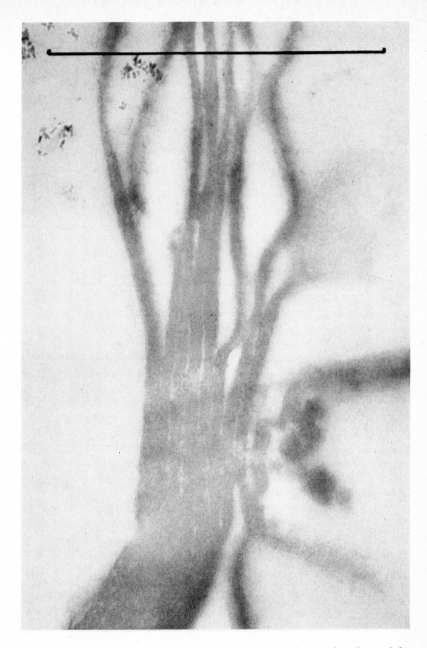

Ephedra monosperma; section through part of the inner laminated layer of an acetolyzed pollen wall (the inner part of the pollen grain is to the left; the black horizontal line indicates 1 μ). × 93,000. (EMG; from Afzelius in Grana palynologica, 1: 2, 1956.)

FITZROYA: see Fig. 42 G, H, p. 26.

GINKGO:—

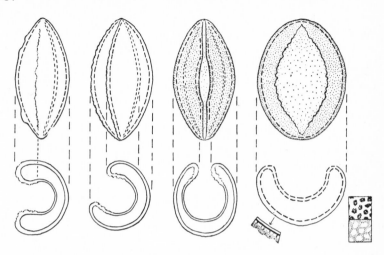

Fig. 32. *Ginkgo biloba*; extreme left detail-figure: pollen grain in lateral, longitudinal view with an outline of the accompanying median transverse section. Second detail-figure from the left: pollen grain slightly tilted with the entrance to the concavity which lodges the tenuitas shown to the left. The remaining figures exhibit the distal face of an unexpanded and an expanded grain. The lower detail figure of the latter gives the outline of a pollen grain in lateral transverse view (owing to an omission a full line uniting the upper extremities of the figure is not shown). × 1000.

GLYPTOSTROBUS:—

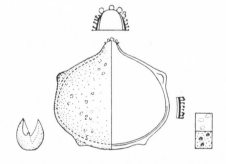

Fig. 33. *Glyptostrobus pensilis*. From left to right: opened grain (× 250); lateral view, surface and optical section (× 1000); exine stratification (× 2000); LO-patterns. Uppermost detail-figure: tenuitas (optical section; × 2000).

GNETUM:—

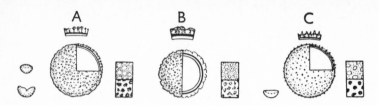

Fig. 34. A, *Gnetum venosum.* — B, *G. africanum.* — C, *G. montanum.*
(From Erdtman in Bot. Notiser 1954.)

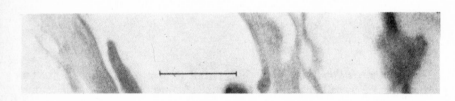

Fig. 35. *Gnetum montanum,* section through part of an acetylyzed, very
compressed pollen grain. To the extreme right is a spinule. The black horizontal line (indicating 1 μ) is drawn within the lumen of the grain. × 21.000.
EMG B. M. Afzelius.

JUNIPERUS, ARCEUTHOS, CHAMAECYPARIS, CUPRESSUS, FITZROYA, LIBOCEDRUS, WIDDRINGTONIA:—

Megaspore membranes: *Chamaecyparis lawsoniana* (Fig. 36, p. 23), *Cupressus arizonica* (Fig. 37, p. 23), *C. whitleyana* (Fig. 38, p. 24), *Juniperus
communis* (Frontispiece and Fig. 39, p. 24), *J. sabina* (Fig. 41, p. 25).

Pollen grains: *Arceuthos drupacea* (Fig. 42 B, p. 26), *Chamaecyparis pisifera*
(Fig. 42 A), *Fitzroya cupressoides* (Fig. 42 G, H), *Juniperus californica* (Fig.
42 D), *J. prostrata* (Fig. 42 E), *Libocedrus decurrens* (Fig. 42 F), *Widdringtonia cupressoides* (Fig. 42 C).

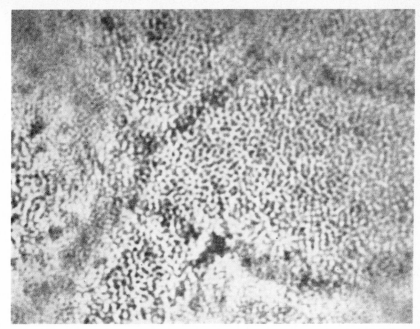

Fig. 36. *Chamaecyparis lawsoniana*; megaspore membrane (surface), phase contrast. × 4000. (From von Lürzer in Grana palynologica, 1: 2, 1956.)

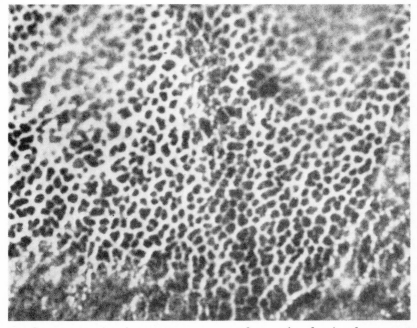

Fig. 37. *Cupressus arizonica*; megaspore membrane (surface), phase contrast. × 4000. (From von Lürzer in Grana palynologica, 1: 2, 1956.)

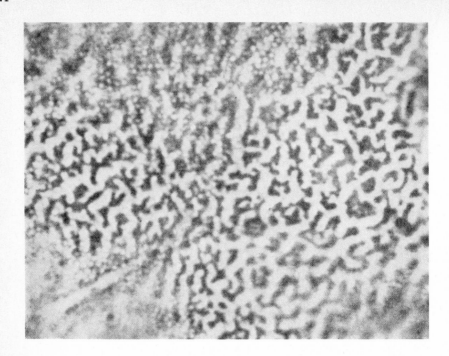

Fig. 38. *Cupressus whitleyana*; megaspore membrane (surface), phase contrast. × 4000. (From von Lürzer in Grana palynologica, 1: 2, 1956.)

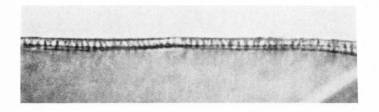

Fig. 39. *Juniperus communis*; megaspore membrane (optical section). × 1000. (For LO-patterns of the membrane surface, see Frontispiece.)

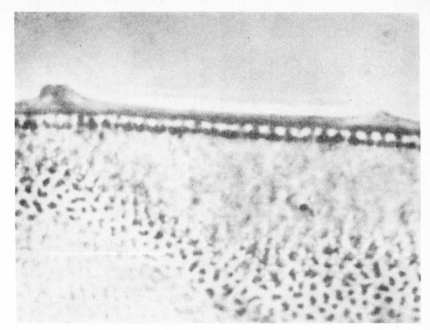

Fig. 40. *Juniperus sabina*; megaspore membrane (optical section), phase contrast. × 4000. (From von Lürzer in Grana palynologica, 1: 2, 1956.)

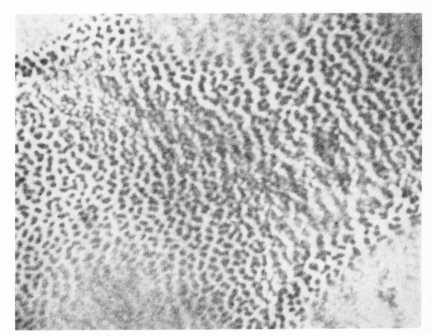

Fig. 41. *Juniperus sabina*; megaspore membrane (surface), phase contrast. × 4000. (From von Lürzer in Grana palynologica, 1: 2, 1956.)

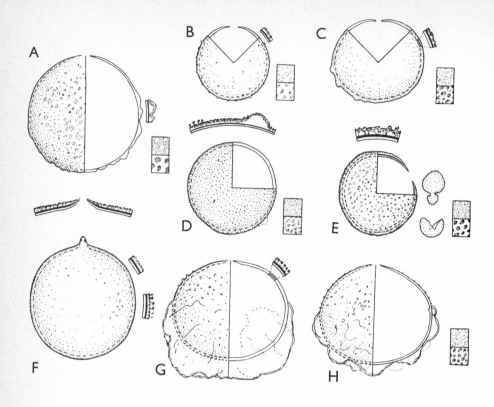

Fig. 42. Cupressaceae. A, *Chamaecyparis pisifera*. B, *Arceuthos drupacea*. C, *Widdringtonia cupressoides*. D, *Juniperus californica*. E, *J. prostrata*. F, *Libocedrus decurrens*. G, H, *Fitzroya cupressoides*. — The main figures (× 1000) exhibit grains in lateral view with (in A–C, and F–H) the distal pole at the top. An aperturoid spot is faintly marked in the upper left-hand quadrant in D. The detail figures show the exine stratification enlarged 2000 times. The detail-figures between the main figure and the LO-patterns in E show an irregular grain (upper detail-figure) and an opened grain (both × 250). H is a *Fitzroya* pollen grain of ± normal type whereas in G a deviating, ± "subsaccate" grain is shown. — Pollen grains of other cupressaceous plants are shown in Figs. 4 (*Actinostrobus*), 11 (*Callitris*), 29 (*Diselma*), 49 (*Neocallitropsis*), 54 (*Pilgerodendron*), and 71 (*Thujopsis*).

KETELEERIA:—

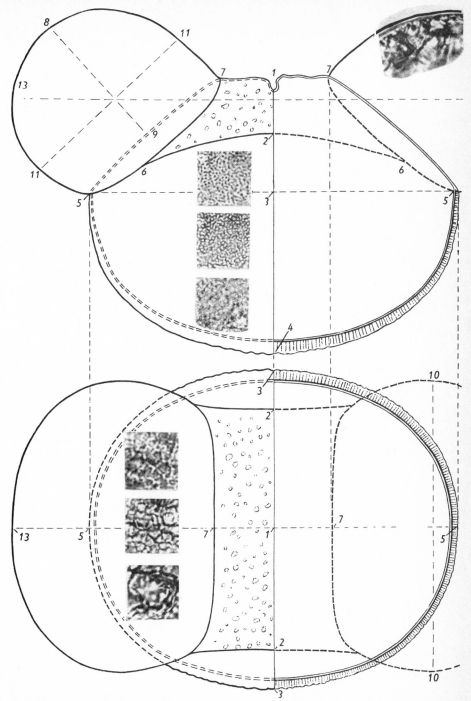

Fig. 43. *Keteleeria davidiana*; lateral, longitudinal view and distal face
(× 1000). For explanation of numerals see Fig. 2, p. 7. (From Erdtman in
Svensk bot. Tidskr. 1954.)

LARIX:—

Megaspore membrane: *Larix occidentalis* (Fig. 44).
Pollen grains: *Larix decidua* f. *polonica* (Fig. 45 B), *L. gmelini* var. *japonica* (Fig. 45 A), *L. occidentalis* (Fig. 45 C).

Fig. 44. *Larix occidentalis*; acetolyzed megaspore wall, optical section (above) and surface (below). × 1000.

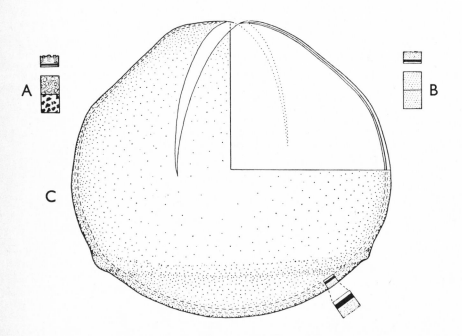

Fig. 45. A, *Larix gmelini* var. *japonica*; exine stratification and LO-patterns. B, *L. decidua* f. *polonica;* exine stratification and "LO-patterns". C, *L. occidentalis;* lateral view, surface and optical section (× 1000).

LIBOCEDRUS: see Fig. 42 F, p. 26.

MACROZAMIA:—

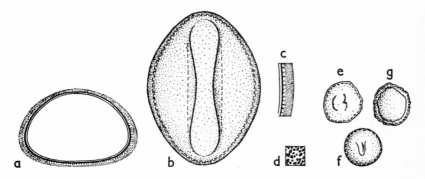

Fig. 46. *Macrozamia spiralis*; a, transverse, equatorial view (optical cross-section); b. distal face; c, exine stratification at amb at right angles to central part of the sulcoid tenuitas; d, pattern caused by infrabaculation (phase contrast); e–g, morphological variants. a, b × 1000, c × 2000, e–g × 250.

METASEQUOIA:—

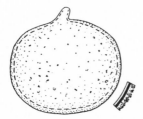

Fig. 47. *Metasequoia glyptostroboides*; lateral view (× 1000) and exine stratification (× 2000).

MICROCACHRYS (Fig. 48 A), MICROSTROBUS (Fig. 48 B):—

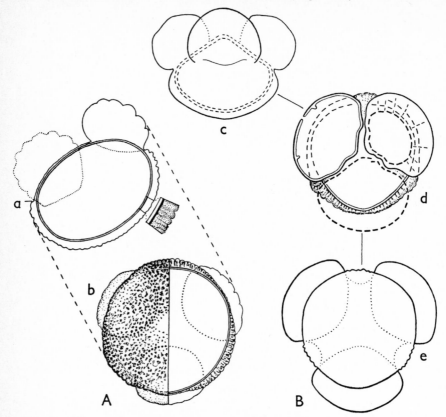

A   B

Fig. 48. A, *Microcachrys tetragona*; a, oblique lateral view (outline; the sexine of the proximal face in the upper right half part of the figure should be thinner); b, proximal face (× 1000). B, *Microstrobus (Pherosphaera) fitzgeraldii*; c, lateral view (outline); d, distal face; e, proximal face (outline; × 1000).

MICROSTROBUS: see Fig. 48 B.

NEOCALLITROPSIS:—

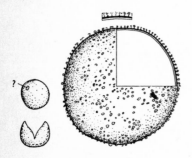

Fig. 49. *Neocallitropsis araucarioides*. Main figure: surface and optical cross-section (× 1000). Details: opened and unopened grains (× 250); exine stratification (× 2000).

NOTHOTAXUS:—

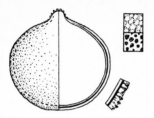

Fig. 50. *Nothotaxus chienii*. From left to right: lateral view, surface and optical section (× 1000); exine stratification (× 2000); LO-patterns.

PHEROSPHAERA: see Fig. 48 B, p. 30.

PHYLLOCLADUS:—

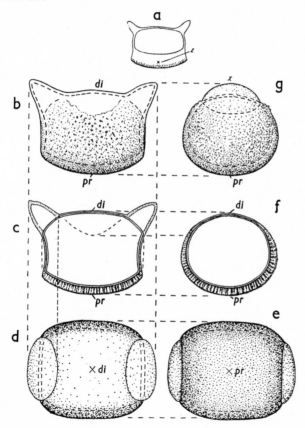

Fig. 51. *Phyllocladus protractus*; a, lateral, longitudinal view of a pollen grain (× 500) with the proximal face covered by a "saccus" (z), possibly an artificial feature resulting from the loosening of the sexine from the nexine; b, g, lateral (longitudinal and transverse) view (surface); c, f, same as b and g, in optical section; d, distal face (× di = distal pole); e, proximal face (× pr = proximal pole). — b–g × 1000.

PICEA:—

Megaspore membrane: *Picea abies* (Fig. 52).
Pollen grains: *Picea jezoensis* (Fig. 53).

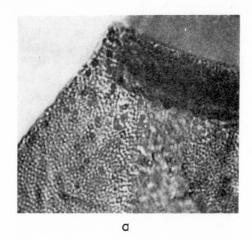

a

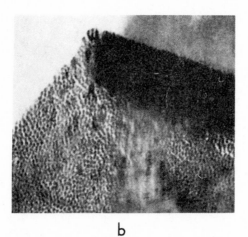

b

Fig. 52. *Picea abies*; part of an acetolyzed megaspore membrane at high (a) and low (b) focus.

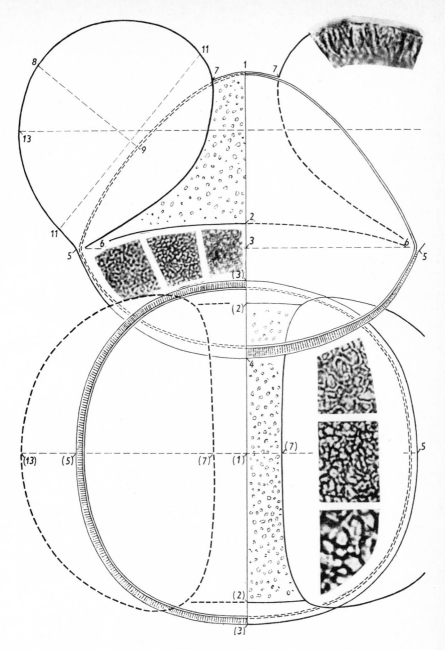

Fig. 53. *Picea jezoensis*; lateral, longitudinal view and distal face (surface and optical section; × 1000); for explanation of numerals see Fig. 2, p. 7. (From Erdtman in Svensk bot. Tidskr. 1954.)

PILGERODENDRON:—

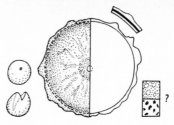

Fig. 54. *Pilgerodendron uviferum*. From left to right: two pollen grains (× 250); distal face (surface and optical section; × 1000); exine stratification (× 2000); LO-patterns.

PINUS:—

P. canariensis (Fig. 55), *P. excelsa* (Fig. 57), *P. mugo* (Fig. 56), *P. peuce* (Fig. 55), *P. pinea* (Fig. 55), *P. thunbergii* (Fig. 58).

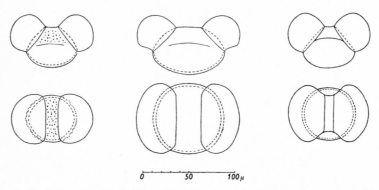

Fig. 55. Left, *Pinus peuce* (subg. Haploxylon). Centre, *P. canariensis* (subg. Diploxylon, sect. Sula). Right, *P. pinea* (subg. Diploxylon, sect. Pinea). × 250.

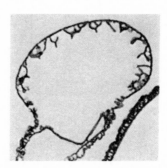

Fig. 56. *Pinus mugo*; section through saccus and, in the lower right-hand corner, part of the exine in the proximal face. About × 1000.

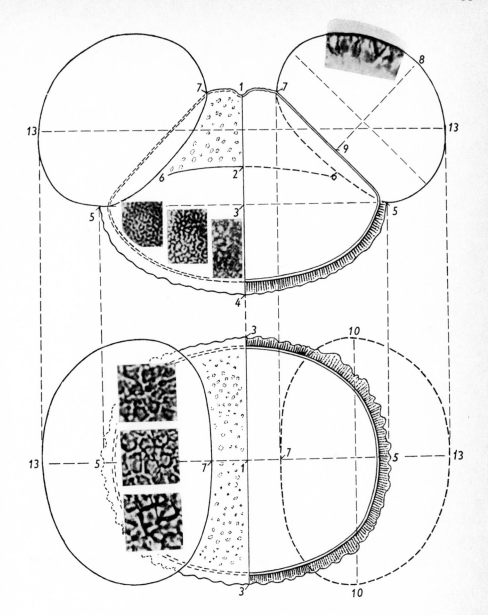

Fig. 57. *Pinus excelsa*; lateral, longitudinal view and distal face (surface and section; × 1000). For explanation of numerals see Fig. 2, p. 7. (From Erdtman in Svensk bot. Tidskr. 1954.)

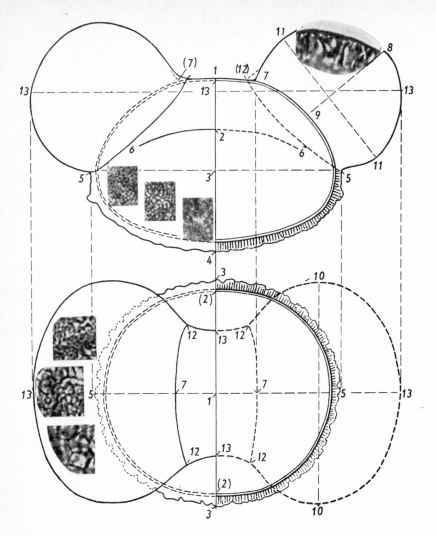

Fig. 58. *Pinus thunbergii*; lateral, longitudinal view and distal face (surface and section; × 1000). For explanation of numerals see Fig. 2, p. 7. (From Erdtman in Svensk bot. Tidskr. 1954.)

PODOCARPUS:—

P. alpinus var. *caespitosus* (Fig. 59 C), *P. angustifolius* var. *wrightii* (Fig. 59 A), *P. blumei* (Fig. 60 B), *P. coriaceus* (Fig. 59 B), *P. dacrydioides* (Fig. 60 A), *P. minor* (Fig. 61 C), *P. nagi* (Fig. 61 D), *P. nubigenus* (Fig. 61 B), *P. wallichianus* (Fig. 61 A).

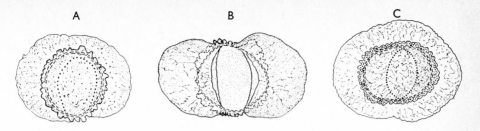

Fig. 59. A, *Podocarpus angustifolius* var. *wrightii*; proximal face. B, *P. coriaceus*; distal face. C, *P. alpinus* var. *caespitosus*; proximal face. × 250.

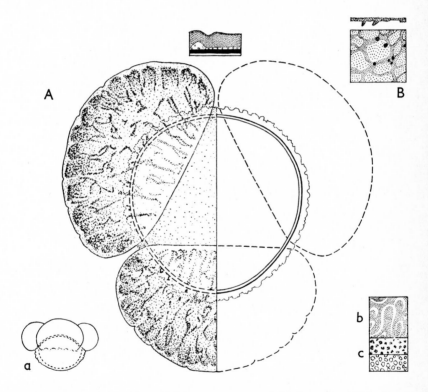

Fig. 60. A, *Podocarpus dacrydioides*; a, equatorial view (× 250); b, saccus pattern at high focus; c, pattern of distal face at high (upper detail figure) and low focus; above the main figure (× 1000) is an optical section through the exine at the amb (× 2000). — B, *P. blumei*; saccus pattern and optical section through the outer wall of the saccus.

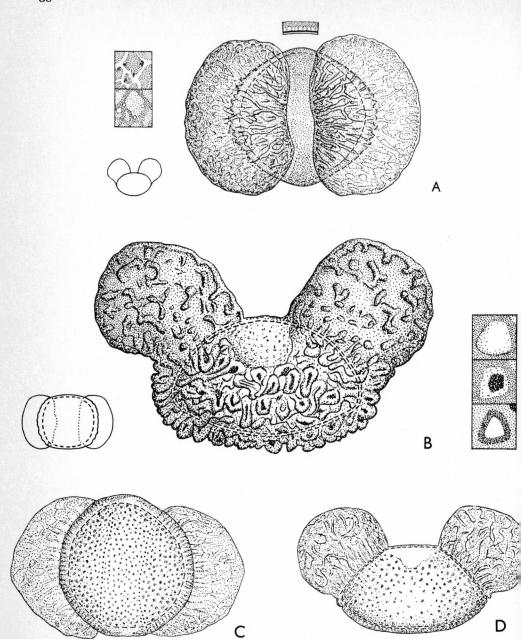

Fig. 61. A, *Podocarpus wallichianus*; lateral, longitudinal view (contour only; × 250), distal face (× 1000). B, *P. nubigenus*. From left to right: proximal face (× 250); lateral, longitudinal view (× 1000); LO-patterns (proximal face). C, *P. minor*; proximal face (× 1000). D, *P. nagi*; lateral, longitudinal view (× 1000).

PSEUDOLARIX:—

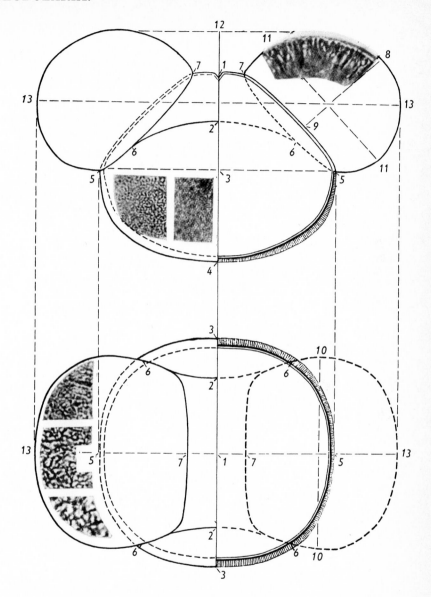

Fig. 62. *Pseudolarix amabilis*; lateral, longitudinal view and distal face (surface and optical section; × 1000). For explanation of numerals see Fig. 2, p. 7. (From Erdtman in Svensk bot. Tidskr. 1954.)

PSEUDOTSUGA:—

Megaspore membrane: *Pseudotsuga taxifolia* (Fig. 63 d).
Pollen grains: *Pseudotsuga taxifolia* (Fig. 63 a–c).

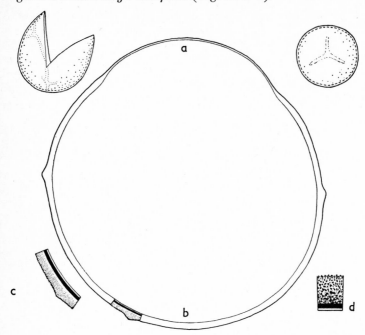

Fig. 63. *Pseudotsuga taxifolia*; a, distal pole (with tenuitas); b, proximal pole; c, part of the microspore exine (optical cross-section, × 2000); d, part of megaspore exine (optical cross-section, × 1000). The upper left-hand detail-figure shows the exine of an opened pollen grain (× 250), the upper right-hand detail-figure a young pollen grain with markings similar to a "tetrad scar".

SAXEGOTHAEA:—

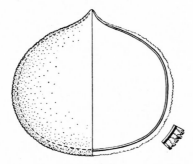

Fig. 64. *Saxegothaea conspicua;* lateral view, surface and optical cross-section (× 1000).

SCIADOPITYS:—

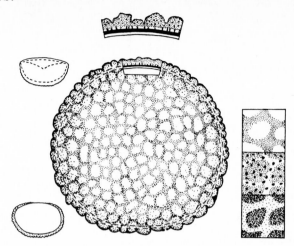

Fig. 65. *Sciadopitys verticillata*; proximal face (× 1000), exine stratification (× 2000), and LO-patterns. Upper left-hand detail: lateral view (distal pole upwards; × 250). Lower left-hand detail: optical section (distal pole upwards; × 250).

SEQUOIA:—

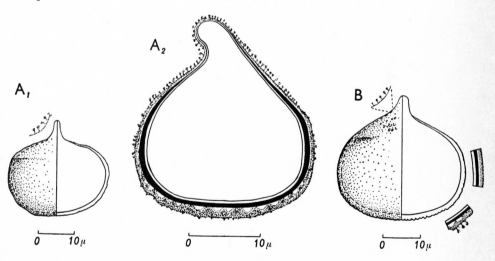

Fig. 66. A, *Sequoia (Sequoiadendron) gigantea*; lateral view, surface and optical cross-sections (A₁ × 1000, A₂ × 2000). B, *S. sempervirens*; lateral view (surface and section; × 1000).

SEQUOIADENDRON: see Fig. 66 A.

42

STANGERIA:—

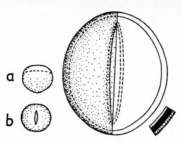

Fig. 67. *Stangeria paradoxa*; distal face (surface and optical section; × 1000); a, lateral view (×250); b, distal face of a grain more broad than long (×250).

TAIWANIA:—

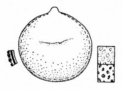

Fig. 68. *Taiwania cryptomerioides.* From left to right: exine stratification (× 2000); lateral view (× 1000); LO-patterns.

TAXODIUM:—

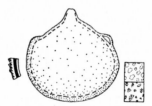

Fig. 69. *Taxodium mucronatum.* From left to right: exine stratification (×2000); lateral view (× 1000); LO-patterns.

TAXUS:—

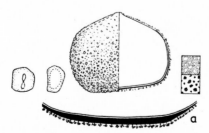

Fig. 70. *Taxus baccata.* From left to right: distal face (× 250); proximal face (× 250); lateral view (surface and optical section; × 1000); LO-patterns. a, exine stratification (× 2000).

THUJOPSIS:—

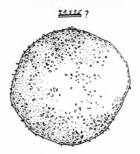

Fig. 71. *Thujopsis dolabrata*; surface (×1000) and exine stratification (×2000).

TORREYA:—

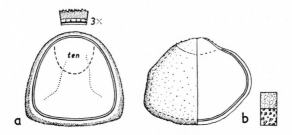

Fig. 72. a, *Torreya californica*; optical section (× 1000) and exine stratification (× 3000). b, *T. nucifera*; lateral view (surface and optical section;
× 1000) and LO-patterns.

TSUGA:—

T. chinensis (Fig. 73 m, o), *T. diversifolia* (Fig 73 g, h), *T. dumosa* (Fig. 73 k),
T. forrestii (Fig. 73 a–f), *T. pattoniana* (Fig. 73 n), *T. sieboldii* (Fig. 73 i, j),
T. yunnanensis (Fig. 73 l).

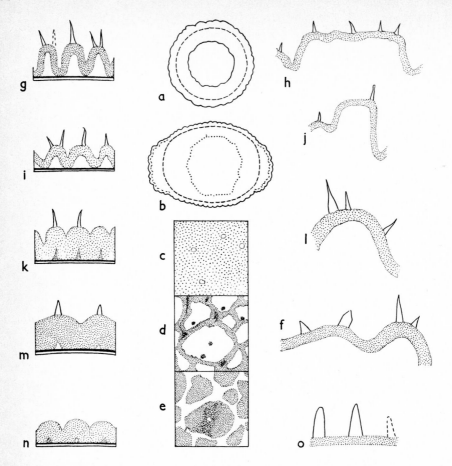

Fig. 73. a–f, *Tsuga forrestii*; a, distal face (outline; × 250); b, proximal face (outline of an aberrant grain; × 250); c–e, LO-patterns [c: four spinules (L); d: the same spinules (O) and upper parts of the undulating tectum (L); e: the fleck near the centre (L) is a small infratectal hollow, also vaguely shown in d (O)]; f, tectum.—Left column (g, i, k, m, n): outline of exine stratification, proximal face (× 2000); g, *T. diversifolia*; i, *T. sieboldii*; k, *T. dumosa*; m, *T. chinensis*; n, *T. pattoniana*. — Right column (h, j, l, f, o): tegillum of the puffy frill (× 2000); h, *T. diversifolia*; j, *T. sieboldii*; l, *T. yunnanensis*; f, *T. forrestii*; o, *T. chinensis*.

WELWITSCHIA: see Fig. 30 C, p. 19.

WIDDRINGTONIA: see Fig. 42 C, p. 26.

PTERIDOPHYTA

Pl. III (facing p. 94); Figs. 74–191.

MEGASPORES

Isoetaceae: Figs. 123–125 (pp. 67, 68).
Pilulariaceae: Fig. 162 d, p. 87.

Selaginellaceae: Pl. III; Figs. 171–173 (pp. 90, 91).

ISOSPORES AND MICROSPORES

Families (in accordance with Engler's Syllabus, 12. Ed., Vol. 1, 1954):

Angiopteridaceae: Fig. 144 A–C (p. 79).
Azollaceae: Fig. 85 (p. 50).
Christenseniaceae: Fig. 144 D (p. 79).
Cyatheaceae: Figs. 78 (p. 47), 96 (p. 56), 112 (p. 62).
Danaeaceae: Fig. 144 F (p. 79).
Dicksoniaceae: Figs. 101 (p. 58), 169 B (p. 90), 186 (p. 95).
Dipteridaceae: Fig. 103 (p. 58).
Equisetaceae: Fig. 106 (p. 60).
Gleicheniaceae: Fig. 114 (p. 63).
Hymenophyllaceae: Fig. 188 (p. 96).
Hymenophyllopsidaceae: Figs. 119, 120 (pp. 65, 66).
Isoetaceae: Figs. 126, 127 (p. 68).
Loxsomaceae: Fig. 136 (p. 73).
Lycopodiaceae: Pl. III; Figs. 138–142 (pp. 75–77), 161 (p. 87).
Marattiaceae: Fig. 144 E (p. 79).
Marsileaceae: Fig. 145 (p. 80).

Matoniaceae: Fig. 159 (p. 86).
Ophioglossaceae: Figs. 89, 90 (pp. 52, 53).
Osmundaceae: Fig. 155 (p. 84).
Parkeriaceae: Figs. 89, 90 (pp. 52, 53).
Pilulariaceae: Fig. 162 a–c (p. 87).
Plagiogyriaceae: Fig. 163 (p. 88).
Polypodiaceae: Figs. 74–77, 81–84, 86–88, 91–95, 97–101, 103–107, 109–111, 115–117, 122, 128–132, 135, 146, 147, 149, 151, 152, 154, 156, 158, 164, 165, 167–169, 183–186, 189–191.
Protocyatheaceae: Figs. 79 (p. 47), 113 (p. 71), 134 (p. 72).
Psilotaceae: Fig. 166 (p. 89).
Salviniaceae: Fig. 170 (p. 90).
Schizaeaceae: Fig. 143 (p. 78).
Selaginellaceae: Figs. 174–182 (pp. 91–94).
Tmesipteridaceae: Fig. 187 (p. 96).

ACROSTICHUM:—

Fig. 74. *Acrostichum aureum* f. *hastaefolium.* Sclerine stratification (× 2000). a, perine; b, cf. sexine; c, cf. nexine.

ACTINIOPTERIS:—

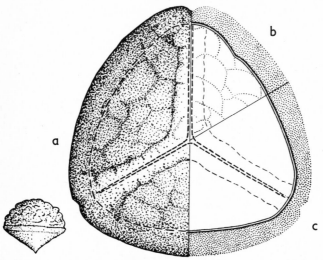

Fig. 75. *Actiniopteris dimorpha.* Spore in lateral view (left; × 250) ; proximal face, surface (a) and optical section (b + c; in b the contours of the verrucae in the distal face are marked; the faint nick in the nexine is quite accidental; × 1000).

ADIANTOPSIS (CHEILANTHES):—

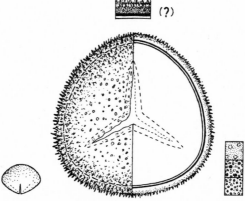

Fig. 76. *Cheilanthes chlorophylla.* From left to right: spore in lateral view (× 250); proximal face (× 1000; surface and optical section); LO-patterns.

ADIANTUM:—

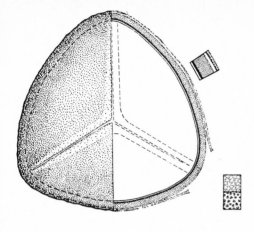

Fig. 77. *Adiantum reniforme*. Proximal face, surface (left) and optical section (right; × 1000).

"ALSOPHILA":—

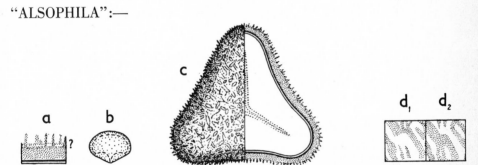

Fig. 78. *Cyathea glabra*; a, sclerine stratification (× 2000); b, spore, lateral view (× 250); c, distal face (× 1000), surface (left) and optical section (right); d₁ and d₂, LO-patterns.

AMPHIDESMIUM:—

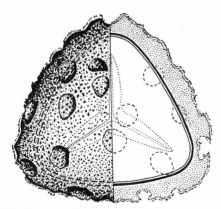

Fig. 79. *Amphidesmium blechnoides*. Distal face (× 1000), surface (left) and optical section (right).

ANARTHROPTERIS:—

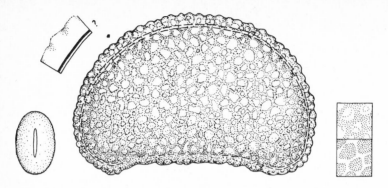

Fig. 80. *Anarthropteris dictyopteris.* From left to right: proximal face (× 250); exine stratification (with a query; × 2000); spore in lateral view (× 1000); LO-patterns.

ANEMIA: see Fig. 143 G–I, p. 78.

ANGIOPTERIS: see Fig. 144 A, p. 79.

ARCHANGIOPTERIS: see Fig. 144 C, p. 79.

ASPLENIOPSIS:—

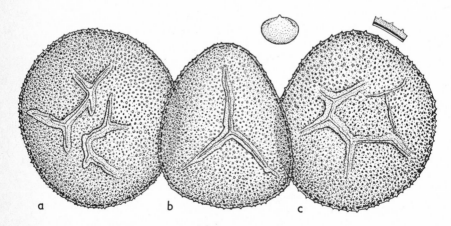

Fig. 81. *Aspleniopsis decipiens*; a and c, deviating spores; b, normal spore (proximal face; × 1000). Upper right-hand details: lateral view (proximal face up; × 250); exine stratification (× 2000).

ASPLENIUM:—

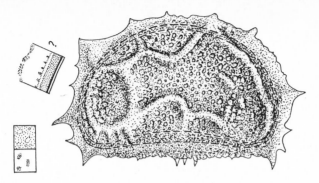

Fig. 82. *Asplenium monanthes*. From left to right: LO-patterns; sclerine stratification (× 2000); spore in lateral view (× 1000).

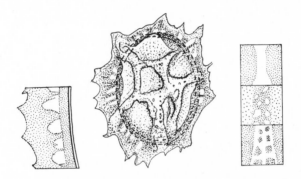

Fig. 83. *Asplenium hemionitis*. From left to right: sclerine stratification (× 2000); distal face (× 1000); LO-patterns.

ATHYRIUM:—

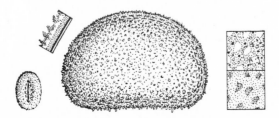

Fig. 84. *Athyrium filix-femina*. From left to right: proximal face (× 250); sclerine stratification (× 2000); spore in lateral view; LO-patterns.

AZOLLA:—

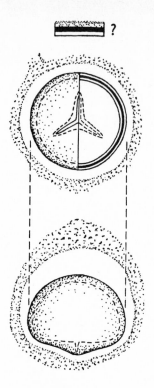

Fig. 85. *Azolla filiculoides*, microspores. From above to below: exine stratification (× 2000); proximal face (× 1000; spore surrounded by perine); spore in lateral view (× 1000).

BLECHNUM:—

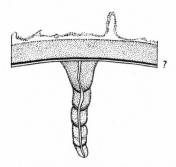

Fig. 86. *Blechnum palmiforme*, part of the sclerine (optical section, × 2000). Attached to the inner surface of the exine is a peculiar (abnormal) process leading into the interior of the spore.

BOLBITIS:—

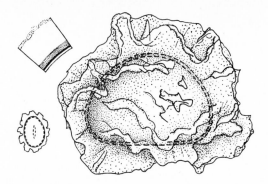

Fig. 87. *Bolbitis turrialbae*. From left to right: proximal face (× 250); sclerine stratification (× 2000); lateral, longitudinal view (× 1000).

BOTRYCHIUM: a note on the spores in *B. simplex* is found in the caption of Fig. 153, p. 83.

BRAINEA:—

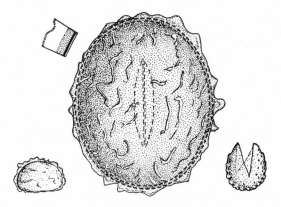

Fig. 88. *Brainea insignis*. From left to right: lateral, longitudinal view (×250); sclerine stratification (× 2000); proximal face (× 1000); deviating spore (× 250).

CERATOPTERIS:—

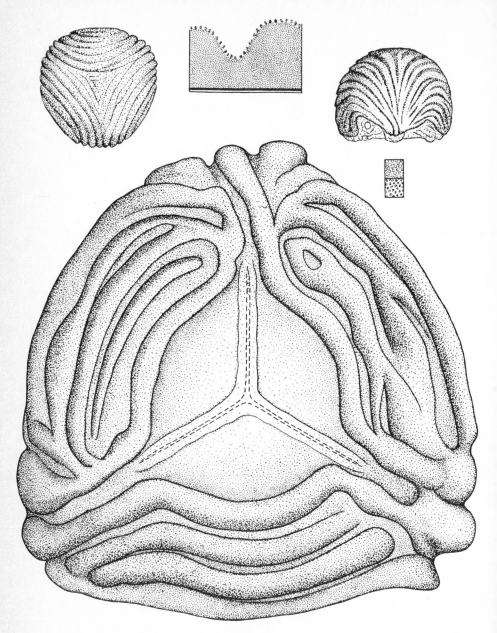

Fig. 89. *Ceratopteris siliquosa*, proximal face (× 1000); upper detail figures (from left to right): distal face (× 250); sclerine stratification (× 2000); lateral view (× 250) and LO-patterns.

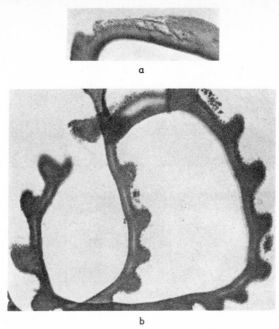

a

b

Fig. 90. *Ceratopteris siliquosa.* Sections through acetolyzed sclerine. The sclerine, as shown in b, consists of a thin perine (the outermost granular layer) and a thick exine faintly subdivided into cf. sexine (showing ± parallel ridges separated by U-shaped valleys) and cf. nexine (of equal thickness throughout). The upper figure (a) intimates that the sexine has a fine (granular) structure. × 700.

CETERACH:—

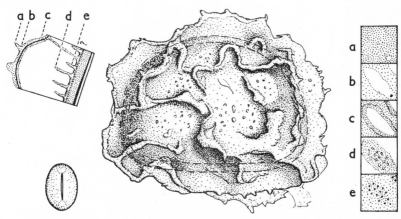

Fig. 91. *Ceterach officinarum.* From left to right: proximal face (× 250); sclerine stratification (× 2000); lateral, longitudinal view (× 1000); LO-patterns.

CHEIROPLEURIA:—

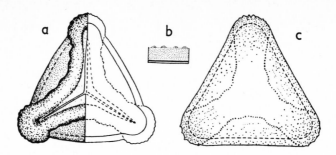

Fig. 92. *Cheiropleuria bicuspis*; a, proximal face (× 1000); b, sclerine stratification (× 2000); c, distal face (× 1000).

CHRISTENSENIA: see Fig. 144 D, p. 79.

CIBOTIUM:—

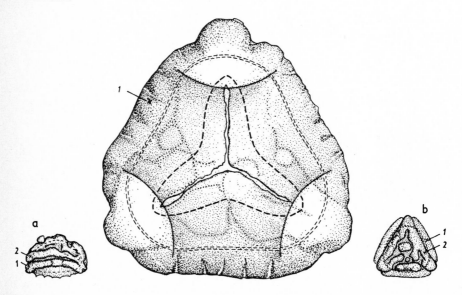

Fig. 93. *Cibotium barometz*, proximal face (× 1000). a, lateral view (× 250); b, distal face (× 250). 1 and 2, respectively, are identical.

CNEMIDARIA:—see Fig. 112 p. 62, and Vol. IV, Fig. 2, p. 218.

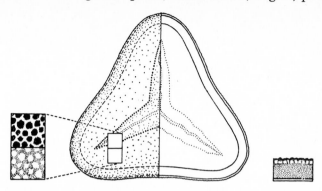

Fig. 94. *"Cnemidaria" speciosa*. From left to right: LO-patterns, distal face (× 1000) and sclerine stratification (× 2000).

CRYPTOGRAMMA:—

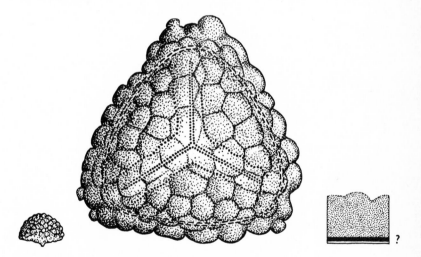

Fig. 95. *Cryptogramma brunoniana*. From left to right: lateral view (× 250), distal face (× 1000), exine stratification (× 2000).

CYATHEA (see also HEMITELIA):—

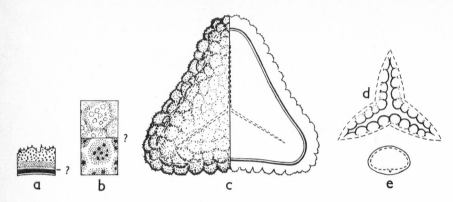

Fig. 96. *Cyathea vestita.* a, sclerine stratification (× 2000); b, LO-patterns; c, distal face (aperture wrongly marked by broken instead of dotted lines); d, laesura (open); e, lateral view (× 250).

CYCLOPHORUS: see PYRROSIA, p. 89.

CYRTOMIUM: see PHANEROPHLEBIA, p. 85.

CYSTODIUM: see Fig. 169 B, p. 90.

CYSTOPTERIS:—

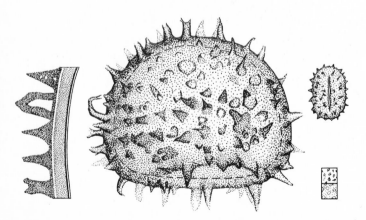

Fig. 97. *Cystopteris fragilis.* From left to right: sclerine stratification (× 2000); lateral, longitudinal view (× 1000); proximal face (× 250) and LO-patterns.

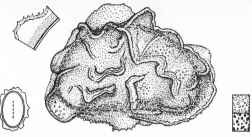

Fig. 98. *Cystopteris fragilis* f. *dickieana*. From left to right: proximal face (optical section, × 250); sclerine stratification (× 2000); lateral, longitudinal view (× 1000); LO-patterns.

DANAEA: see Fig. 144 F, p. 79.

DAVALLIA:—

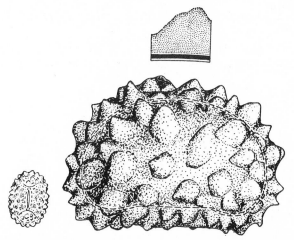

Fig. 99. *Davallia canariensis*. Proximal face (× 250); lateral, longitudinal view (× 1000), and exine stratification (× 2000).

DENNSTAEDTIA:—

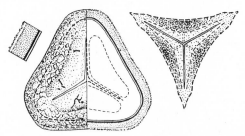

Fig. 100. *Dennstaedtia punctilobula*. From left to right: sclerine stratification (× 2000); proximal face, surface and section (× 1000); analysis of laesura.

DICKSONIA:—

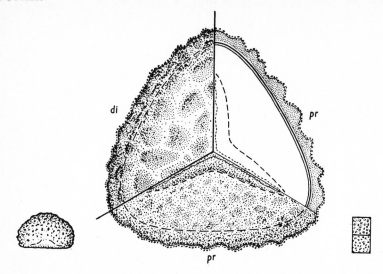

Fig. 101. *Dicksonia youngiae.* From left to right: lateral view (× 250); distal (di) and proximal (pr; surface and optical section) face; LO-patterns.

DIPLAZIUM:—

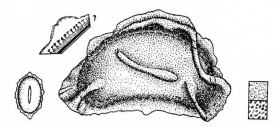

Fig. 102. *Diplazium proliferum.* From left to right: proximal face (× 250); sclerine stratification (× 2000); lateral, longitudinal view (× 1000); LO-patterns.

DIPTERIS:—

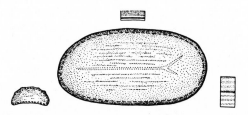

Fig. 103. *Dipteris chinensis.* From left to right: lateral, longitudinal view (× 250); distal face (× 1000) and exine stratification (× 2000); LO-patterns.

DRYMOGLOSSUM:—

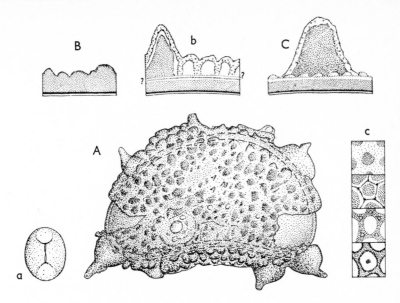

Fig. 104. A, *Drymoglossum heterophyllum*, lateral, longitudinal view (× 1000); a, proximal face (× 250); b and C, sclerine stratification (× 2000); c, LO-patterns. B, *D. carnosum*, sclerine stratification (× 2000).

DRYNARIA:—

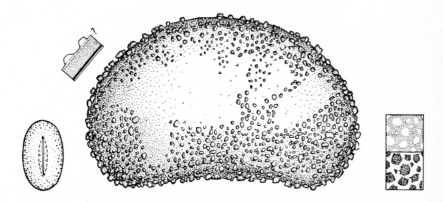

Fig. 105. *Drynaria fortunei*. From left to right: proximal face (× 250); sclerine stratification (× 2000); lateral, longitudinal view (× 1000); LO-patterns.

DRYOPTERIS:—

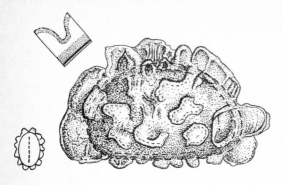

Fig. 106. *Dryopteris filix-mas.*
From left to right: proximal
face (optical section, × 250);
sclerine stratification (× 2000);
equatorial, longitudinal view
(× 1000).

ELAPHOGLOSSUM:—

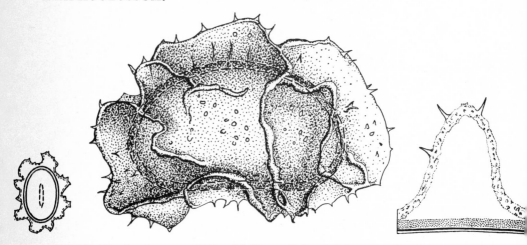

Fig. 107. *Elaphoglossum vieillardii.* From left to right: proximal face (optical
section, × 250); lateral, longitudinal view (× 1000); sclerine stratification
(× 2000).

EQUISETUM:—

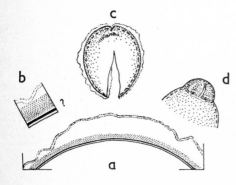

Fig. 108. *Equisetum giganteum.* a, part
of sclerine of an acetolyzed spore, optical cross-section (× 1000); amplec-
tators ("elaters", "hapters") dissolved;
b, sclerine stratification (× 2000); c,
opened spore (× 250); d, part of an
abnormal spore tetrad (one large, three
small spores; × 250).

GRAMMITIS:—

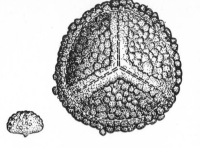

Fig. 109. *Grammitis deplanchei*. From left to right: lateral view (× 250); proximal face (× 1000); LO-patterns.

GYMNOGRAMME:—

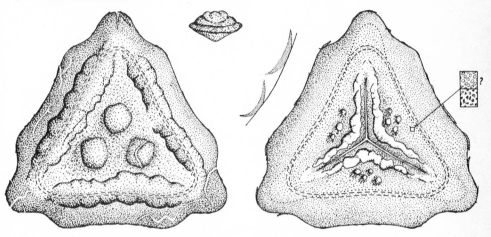

Fig. 110. *Gymnogramme (Eriosorus) congesta*. From left to right: distal face (× 1000); lateral view (× 250); cf. perine fragments (optical section, × 2000); proximal face (× 1000) and LO-patterns.

HEMIONITIS:—

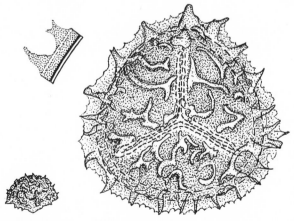

Fig. 111. *Hemionitis arifolia*. From left to right: lateral view (× 250); sclerine stratification (× 2000); proximal face (× 1000).

"HEMITELIA":—

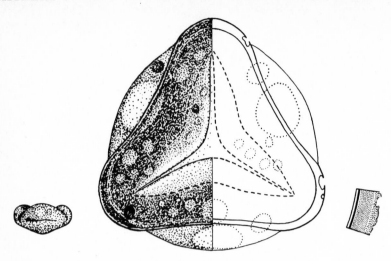

Fig. 112. *"Cnemidaria (Cyathea) Subarachnoidea"*: lateral view ($\times$ 250), proximal face (surface and optical cross section, $\times$ 1000); sclerine stratification ($\times$ 2000). From Erdtman in Potonié, Svensk bot. Tidskr. 1954.

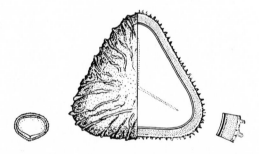

Fig. 113. *Cyathea Deyrichiana*. From left to right: lateral view ($\times$ 250); distal face, surface and optical cross-section ($\times$ 1000); sclerine stratification ($\times$ 2000).

HICRIOPTERIS (Fig. 114 C), PLATYZOMA (Fig. 114 D), STICHERUS (Fig. 114 B), STROMATOPTERIS (Fig. 114 A):—

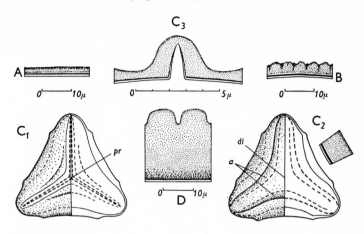

Fig. 114. Gleicheniaceae. A, *Stromatopteris moniliformis*, sclerine stratification. B, *Sticherus penniger*, sclerine stratification. C, *Hicriopteris laevissima*; C_1, proximal face; C_2, distal face; C_3, part of laesura (optical cross-section), C_4, LO-patterns of same. D, *Platyzoma microphyllum*, sclerine stratification. — A, B, D × 800, C_1 and C_2 × 1000, C_3 × 4600.

HISTIOPTERIS:—

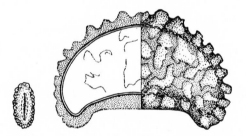

Fig. 115. *Histiopteris incisa*; proximal face (× 250) and lateral, longitudinal view (optical cross-section and surface; × 1000).

HOLTTUMIELLA:—

Fig. 116. *Holttumiella flabellivenium*. Three spores of a tetrad still slightly adhering. × 700.

HUMATA:—

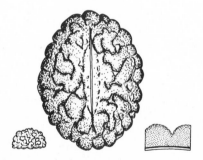

Fig. 117. *Humata gaimardiana*. From left to right: lateral, longitudinal view (× 250); proximal face (× 1000); sclerine stratification (× 2000).

HYMENOGLOSSUM: see Fig. 188 C, p. 96.

HYMENOLEPIS:—

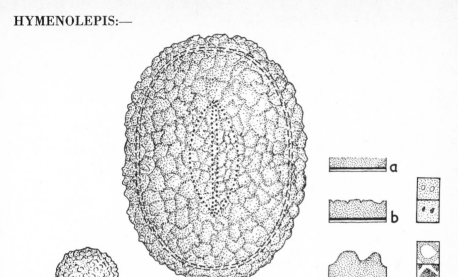

Fig. 118. *Hymenolepis spicata.* From left to right: lateral, longitudinal view
(× 250); distal face (× 1000); a–c, exine stratification showing the successive
increase in thickness (× 2000); LO-patterns.

HYMENOPHYLLOPSIS (Figs. 119, 120):—

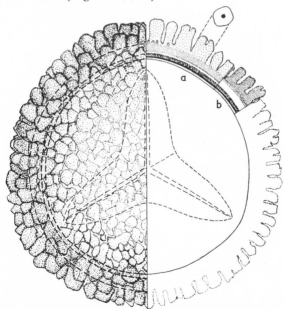

Fig. 119. *Hymenophyllopsis asplenioides,* proximal face, surface and optical
cross-section (× 1000). In some spores the sclerine stratification appears
as indicated at a, and in other spores as indicated at b.

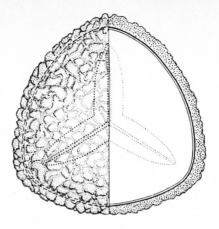

Fig. 120. *Hymenophyllopsis dejecta*; distal face (surface and optical cross-section). × 1000.

HYMENOPHYLLUM (see also Fig. 188 C, p. 96):—

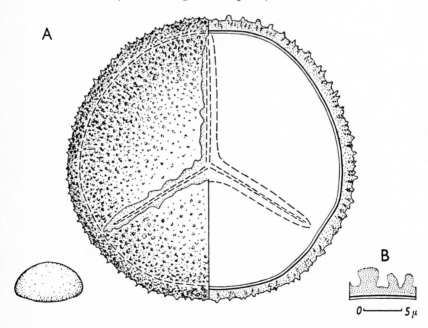

Fig. 121. A, *Hymenophyllum recurvum*; lateral view (× 250) and proximal face, surface and optical cross-section (× 1000). B, *H. peltatum*, exine stratification (× 2000).

HYPOLEPIS:—

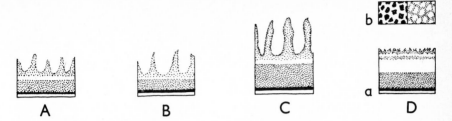

Fig. 122. Sclerine stratification in *Hypolepis*. A, *H. repens*. B, *H. tenuifolia*. C, *H. rugosula*. D:a, *H. distans*. (× 2000). — LO-patterns at high (left) and low (right) focus in *H. distans* are shown in D:b.

ISOËTES:—

Megaspores: *Isoëtes durieui* (Fig. 123), *I. echinosporum* (Figs. 124, 125). Microspores: *Isoëtes adspersa* (Fig. 126), *I. baetica* (Fig. 127).

Fig. 123. *Isoëtes durieui*, part of megaspore wall (section). × 1000.

Fig. 124. *Isoëtes echinospora;* part of megaspore wall (optical section). The inner contour of the silicified perine is faintly seen left and right of the cf. sexinous outgrowth in the centre of the figure. The "sexine" is underlain by thinner "nexine". × 2000.

Fig. 125. *Isoëtes echinosporum*, acetolyzed megaspore embedded in glycerine jelly (× 125). In some places the spiny perine is faintly shown.

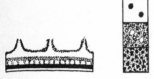

Fig. 126. *Isoëtes adspersa*; sclerine stratification and LO-patterns. A thin cf. perine with hollow, tapering processes, open at top (OL), is underlain by an exine consisting of a tectame and infrabaculate sexine (LO = bacula) and nexine.

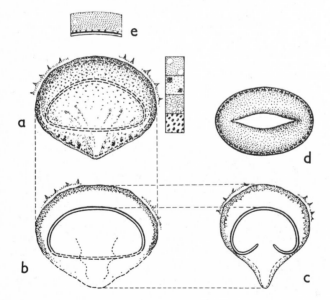

Fig. 127. *Isoëtes baetica*. a, lateral, longitudinal view (surface); b, lateral, longitudinal view (optical section); c, lateral transverse view (optical section); c, lateral transverse view (optical section); d, polar view (proximal face; sculptine not included); e, exine from a young spore with sexine still adhering to the nexine; × 4000 (a–d × 1000).

ISOLOMA:—

Fig. 128. *Isoloma divergens.* From left to right: proximal face (×250); lateral, longitudinal view (× 1000); exine stratification.

JAMESONIA:—

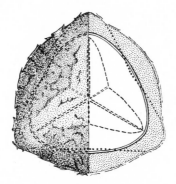

Fig. 129. *Jamesonia imbricata*; proximal face, surface and optical section (× 1000).

LASTREA:—

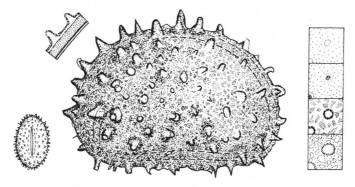

Fig. 130. *Lastrea thelypteris.* From left to right: proximal face (× 250); sclerine stratification (× 2000); lateral, longitudinal view (× 1000); LO-patterns.

LEPTOLEPIA:—

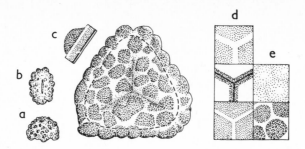

Fig. 131. *Leptolepia novae-zelandiae*; proximal face (× 1000). — a, equatorial view (× 250); b, proximal face of monolete spore (× 250); c, sclerine stratification showing perine (densely dotted) on the outside of the exine; d, proximal pole at various focuses from high (above) to low; e, general surface of spore at different focuses. — N.B. Exceptionally, the "verrucae" in the main figure are shown at low focus (i.e. dark), and not, as otherwise in this book, at high focus (bright).

LEPTOPTERIS: see Fig. 155 G, p. 84.

LINDSAEA:—

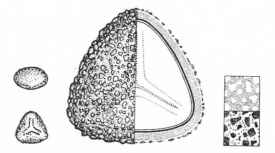

Fig. 132. *Lindsaea orbiculata*. From left to right: lateral view and proximal face (both × 250); distal face (× 1000); LO-patterns.

LOPHOSORIA (Figs. 133, 134):—

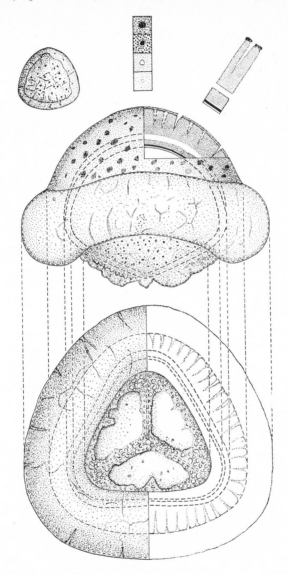

Fig. 133. *Lophosoria quadripinnata* (Puerto Rico; Sintenis 1333, ex herb. Paris); lateral view (surface and section) and proximal face (× 1000). At top, from left to right: distal face (× 250), LO-patterns, sclerine stratification (× 2000).

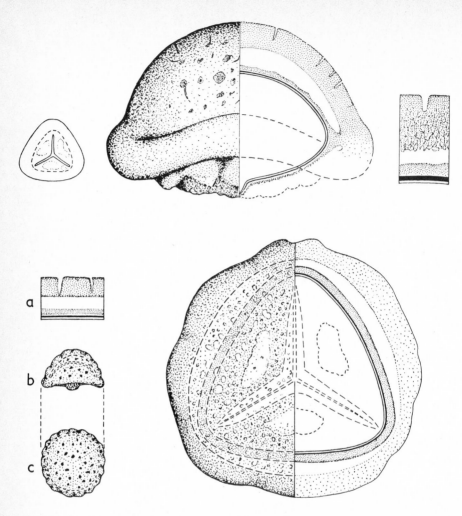

Fig. 134. *Lophosoria quadripinnata*. Upper figures (Weberbauer 1333; ex herb. Berlin), from left to right: proximal face (× 250); lateral view (× 1000); sclerine stratification (× 2000). Lower figures: proximal face of a *Lophosoria* spore found in a slide made from *Serpyllopsis caespitosa* var. *densifolia* (collected by C. Skottsberg in the Juan Fernandez Islands August 27th, 1908); a, sclerine stratification (× 1000); b, lateral view (× 250); c, distal face (× 250).

LORINSERIA:—

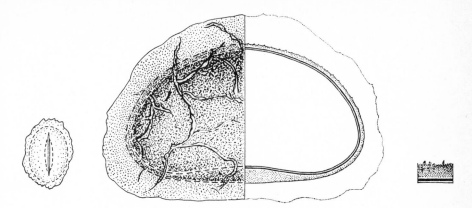

Fig. 135. *Lorinseria areolata*. From left to right: proximal face (× 250); lateral, longitudinal view (× 1000); exine stratification (perine not considered; × 2000).

LOXSOMA:—

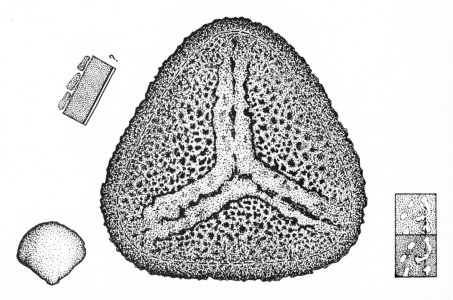

Fig. 136. *Loxsoma cunninghamii*. From left to right: lateral view (× 250); sclerine stratification (× 2000); proximal face (× 1000); LO-patterns.

LOXSOMOPSIS:—

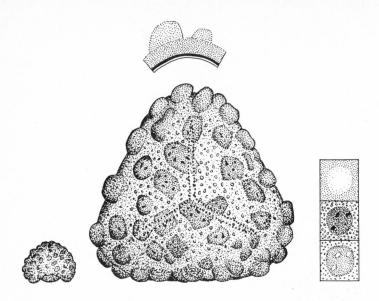

Fig. 137. *Loxsomopsis lehmannii*. Lateral view (× 250), distal face (× 1000),
and LO-patterns. At top sclerine stratification (× 2000).

LYCOPODIUM:—

L. clavatum [Pl. III (facing p. 94); Figs. 138 B, 142], *L. densum* (Fig. 139),
L. diaphanum (Fig. 138 A), *L. drummondii* (Fig. 140), *L. insulare* Fig. 141).

Fig. 138. A, *Lycopodium diaphanum*; a + b, distal face (a, at high, b, at low
adjustment of the microscope; the different foci correspond to levels a_1 and
b_1 in Fig. A: d; c, proximal face (main part of figure: surface view at high
adjustment; upper right-hand part: section through the exine; d and e: outline of exine stratification at distal pole, e along the AMB).—B, *L. clavatum*:
detail corresponding to that in *L. diaphanum* shown in Fig. A: e. — × 2000
(A: a–c), × 4000 (A: d and e; B), × 500 (lower left-hand detail figure=spore
of *L. diaphanum* in lateral view, distal face up). — From Erdtman in Afzelius, Erdtman and Sjöstrand, Svensk bot. Tidskr. 1954.

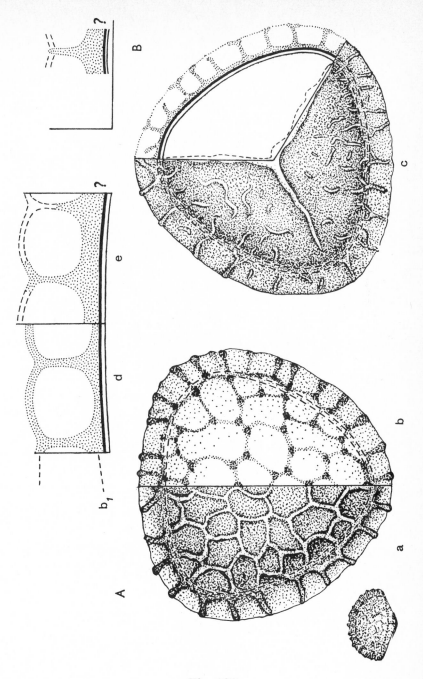

Fig. 138.

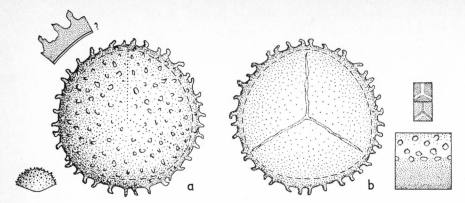

Fig. 139. *Lycopodium densum*; a, distal, b, proximal face (both × 1000); lower right detail-figure: part of exine surface at the transition between the distal and the proximal face.

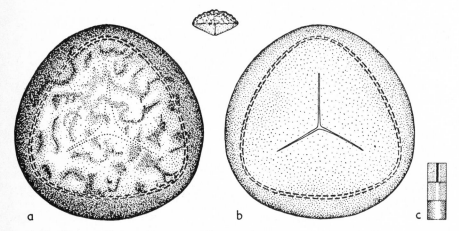

Fig. 140. *Lycopodium drummondii*; a, distal, b, proximal face (× 1000); c, part of laesura at different adjustments of the microscope from high to low.

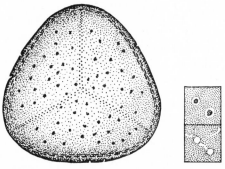

Fig. 141. *Lycopodium insulare*; distal face (× 1000) and LO-patterns.

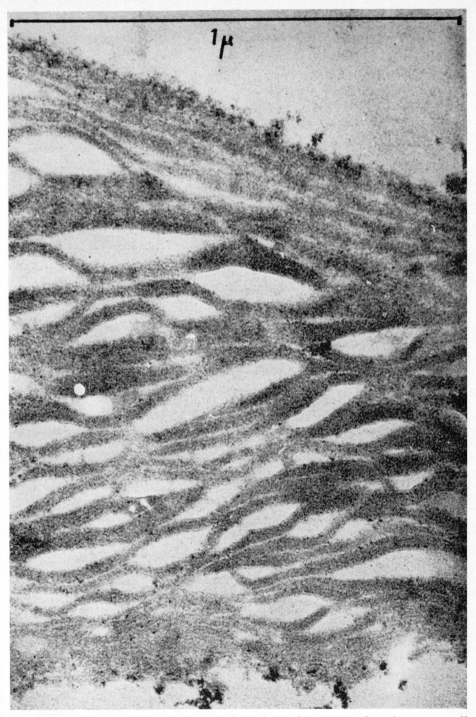

Fig. 142. *Lycopodium clavatum*; section through an acetolyzed spore wall
($\times$ 125,000) exhibiting the fine, granular-lamellar, structure of the outer part
of the exine. The distinct lamellae shown in this figure are multiples of fine
lamellae (thickness 50–60 Å). Each of these consists of a single layer of
granules. EMG B. M. Afzelius. (From Grana palynologica, 1: 2, 1956.)

LYGODIUM (Fig. 143 A–D), ANEMIA (Fig. 143 G–I), MOHRIA (Fig. 143 J), SCHIZAEA (Fig. 143 E, F):—

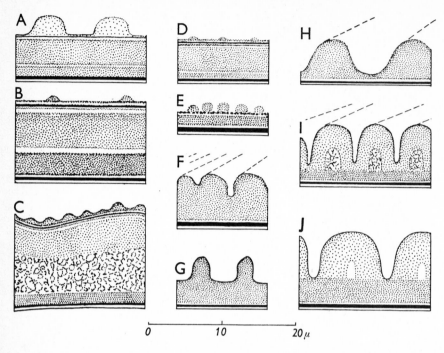

Fig. 143. Schizaeaceae, sclerine stratification (× 2000). A, *Lygodium circinnatum.* B, *L. volubile.* C, *L. micans.* D, *L. japonicum.* E, *Schizaea fluminensis.* F, *S. melanesica.* G, *Anemia phyllitidis.* H, *A. adiantifolia.* I, *A. anthriscifolia.* J, *Mohria caffrorum.* (From Erdtman in Svensk bot. Tidskr. 1954.)

MACROGLENA: see Fig. 188 B, p. 96.

MACROGLOSSUM: see Fig. 144 B, p. 79.

MARATTIA (Fig. 144 E), ANGIOPTERIS (Fig. 144 A), ARCHANGIOPTERIS (Fig. 144 C), CHRISTENSENIA (Fig. 144 D), DANAEA (Fig. 144 F), MACROGLOSSUM (Fig. 144 B):—

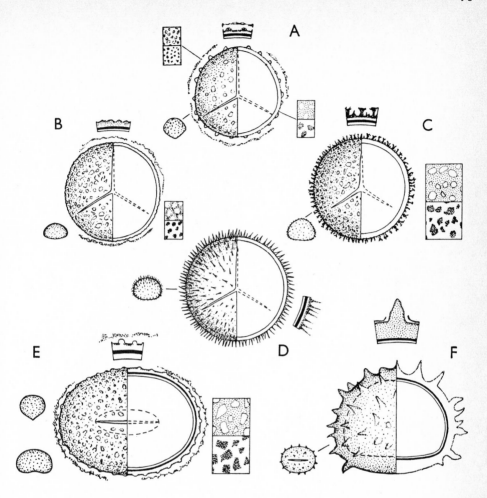

Fig. 144. Marattiales. A, *Angiopteris longifolia*; proximal face (surface and optical section; × 1000). B, *Macroglossum alidae*; proximal face (surface and optical section; × 1000); C, *Archangiopteris henryi*; proximal face (surface and optical section; × 1000). D, *Christensenia aesculifolia*; proximal face (surface and optical section; × 1000); to the left two spores in lateral, transverse and lateral, longitudinal view (× 250). E, *Marattia fraxinea*; proximal face (surface and optical cross-section; × 1000); to the left two spores in transverse lateral and in longitudinal lateral view (× 250). F, *Danaea elliptica*; lateral, longitudinal view (× 1000), proximal face (× 250) and sclerine stratification (× 2000). (From Erdtman in Svensk bot. Tidskr. 1954.)

MARSILEA:—

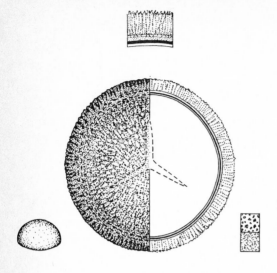

Fig. 145. *Marsilea aegyptiaca*, microspore. From left to right: lateral view (× 250); proximal face (surface and optical section; × 1000); sclerine stratification (× 2000) and LO-patterns.

MATTEUCIA:—

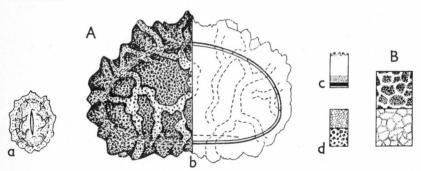

Fig. 146. A, *Matteucia struthiopteris*; a, proximal face (× 250); b, lateral, longitudinal view (surface and optical section; × 1000); c, sclerine stratification (× 2000); d, LO-patterns. B, *M. orientalis*, LO-patterns.

MICROLEPIA:—

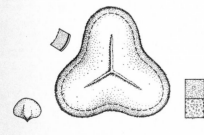

Fig. 147. *Microlepia hirta*. From left to right: lateral view (× 250); sclerine stratification (× 2000); proximal face (× 1000); LO-patterns.

MOHRIA: see Fig. 143 J, p. 78.

NEGRIPTERIS:—

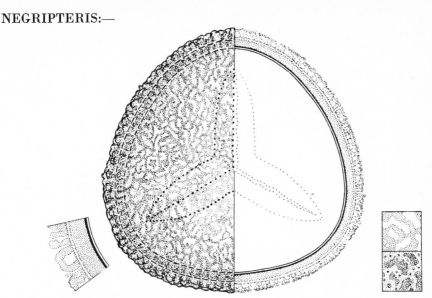

Fig. 148. *Negripteris sciana*. From left to right: sclerine stratification (× 2000); distal face (surface and optical section; × 1000); LO-patterns.

NEPHROLEPIS:—

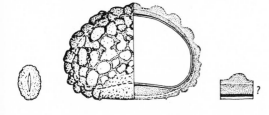

Fig. 149. *Nephrolepis cordifolia*. From left to right: proximal face (×250); lateral, longitudinal view (× 1000); sclerine stratification; (× 2000).

OLEANDRA:—

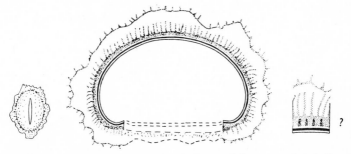

Fig. 150. *Oleandra neriiformis*. From left to right: proximal face (× 250); lateral view (median optical section; × 1000); sclerine stratification (× 2000).

ONOCLEA:—

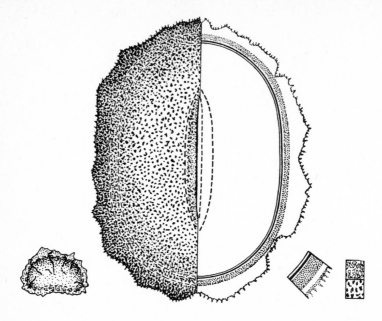

Fig. 151. *Onoclea sensibilis*. From left to right: lateral, longitudinal view
(× 250); proximal face (surface and optical section; × 1000); sclerine
stratification; × 2000); LO-patterns.

ONYCHIUM:—

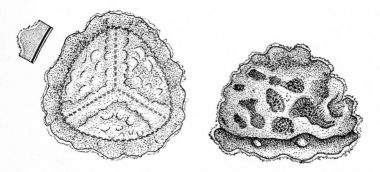

Fig. 152. *Onychium japonicum*. From left to right: sclerine stratification
(× 2000); proximal face (× 1000); lateral view (× 1000).

OPHIOGLOSSUM:—

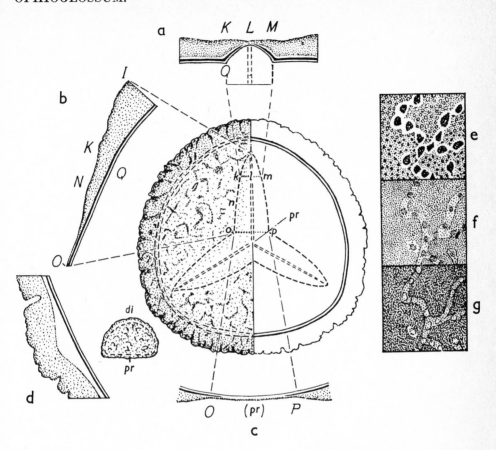

Fig. 153. *Ophioglossum coriaceum*. Main figure: proximal face (× 1000), surface and optical section; a–d, sections through the exine (× 2000: a, b, and c are sections along the lines *klm, ikno,* and *op* in the main figure (*klm* corresponds to the letters KLM in fig. a etc.) whereas d exhibits a part of the exine with the sexine locally severed from the nexine (in *Botrychium simplex* transitions have been seen from spores with the sexine adhering to the nexine, as in the main figure above, to such where the sexine is almost completely separated from the nexine—due to the chemical treatment— imparting a ± pansaccate appearance to the spore); e–g, LO-patterns at high, medium, and low focus. Between d and the main figure is as spore seen from the side (× 250; di, distal, pr, proximal pole).—From Erdtman in Svensk bot. Tidskr. 1954.

ORMOLOMA (Fig. 154 A), ORTHIOPTERIS (Fig. 154 B):—

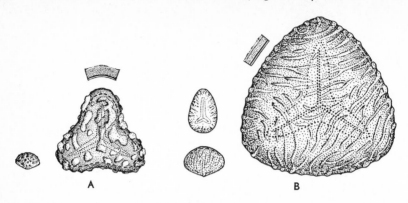

A   B

Fig. 154. A, *Ormoloma imrayana*; lateral view (× 250), distal face (×1000), and sclerine stratification (× 2000). B, *Orthiopteris inaequalis*; proximal face (× 1000), exine stratification (× 2000), and—to the left—spore in lateral view (× 250) and proximal face of an aberrant spore (× 250).

ORTHIOPTERIS: see Fig. 154 B.

OSMUNDA (Fig. 155 A–E), LEPTOPTERIS (Fig. 155 G), TODEA (Fig. 155 F):—

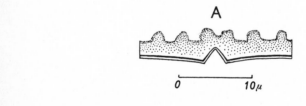

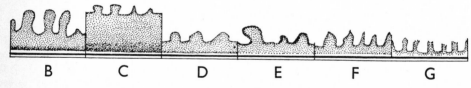

B   C   D   E   F   G

Fig. 155. Osmundaceae, exine stratification (× 2000). A, *Osmunda cinnamomea*, part of exine in proximal face (with laesura). B–G, part of exine in distal face; B, *Osmunda regalis* (subgen. Euosmunda); C, *O. banksiifolia* (subgen. Pleasium); D, *O. cinnamomea* (subgen. Osmundastrum); E, *O. claytoniana* (subgen. Osmundastrum); F, *Todea barbara*; G, *Leptopteris superba*.

PELLAEA:—

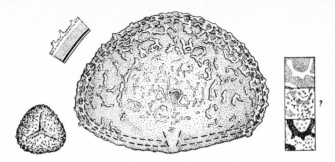

Fig. 156. *Pellaea viridis.* From left to right: proximal face (× 250); sclerine stratification (× 2000); lateral view (× 1000); LO-patterns.

PERANEMA:—

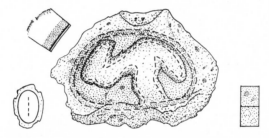

Fig. 157. *Peranema cyatheoides.* From left to right: proximal face (× 250); sclerine stratification (× 2000); spore in lateral, longitudinal view (× 1000); LO-patterns (OL-pattern due to small perforations in the perine).

PHANEROPHLEBIA:—

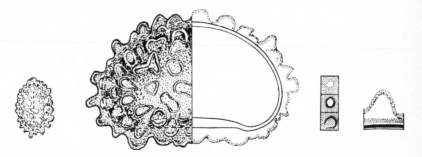

Fig. 158. *Phanerophlebia caryotidea.* From left to right: proximal face (× 250); spore in lateral, longitudinal view (surface and optical section; × 1000); LO-patterns; sclerine stratification (× 2000).

PHANEROSORUS:—

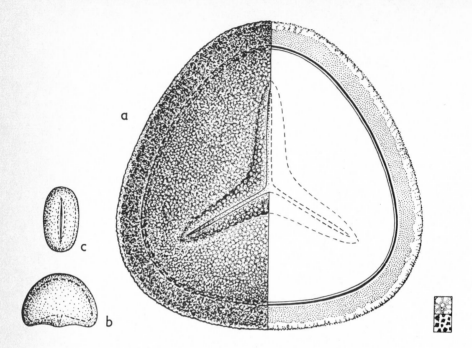

Fig. 159. *Phanerosorus major*; a, proximal face, surface and optical sections (× 1000); b, spore in lateral view (× 250); c, monolete spore, proximal face (× 250). The LO-pattern in the lower right-hand corner is due to the thin perinous cover.

PHLEBODIUM:—

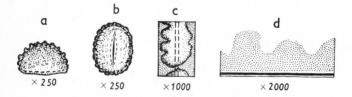

Fig. 160. *Phlebodium aureum*; a, spore in lateral, longitudinal view; b, proximal face; c, part of proximal face with laesura (broken lines); d, exine stratification.

PHYLLOGLOSSUM:—

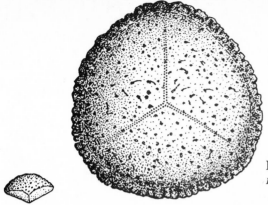

Fig. 161. *Phylloglossum drum-mondii*; lateral view (× 250) and distal face (× 1000).

PILULARIA:—

Megaspore: *Pilularia globulifera* (Fig. 162 d).
Microspores: *Pilularia globulifera* (Fig. 162 a–c).

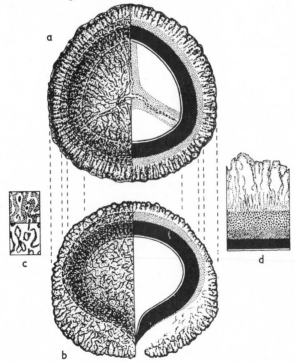

Fig. 162. *Pilularia globulifera.* a–c, microspore. a, proximal face (surface and optical cross-section; × 1000); b, lateral view (surface and optical cross-section; × 1000); c, LO-patterns; d, megaspore, sclerine stratification (× 2000; cf. also Grana palynologica, 1: 2, 1956, Pl. I, Fig. 13, facing p. 126).

PLAGIOGYRIA:—

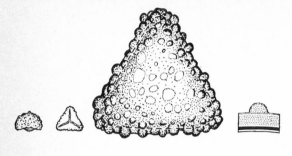

Fig. 163. *Plagiogyria henryi.*
From left to right: lateral view
(×250); proximal face (×250);
distal face (× 250); sclerine
stratification (× 2000).

PLATYCERIUM:—

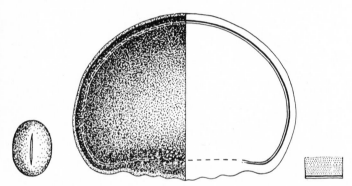

Fig. 164. *Platycerium madagascariense.* From left to right: proximal face
(× 250); lateral view (surface and optical cross-section; × 1000); sclerine
stratification (× 2000).

PLATYZOMA: see Fig. 114 D, p. 63.

POLYBOTRYA:—

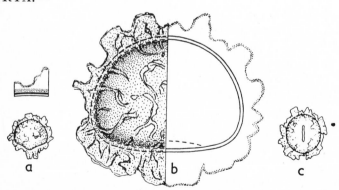

Fig. 165. *Polybotrya appendiculata*; a, lateral, transverse view (× 250);
b, lateral, longitudinal view (surface and optical section, × 1000); c, proximal face (× 250); upper left-hand detail: sclerine stratification (× 2000).

PSILOTUM:—

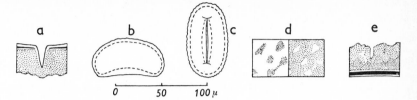

Fig. 166. *Psilotum nudum*; a, laesura (optical cross-section; × 2000); b, lateral, longitudinal view (× 250); c, proximal face (× 250); d, LO-patterns; e, sclerine stratification (× 2000).

PTERIDIUM:—

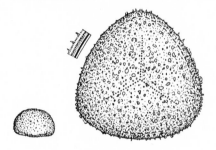

Fig. 167. *Pteridium aquilinum*. From left to right: lateral view (× 250); sclerine stratification (× 2000); distal face (× 1000).

PYRROSIA:—

Fig. 168. *Pyrrosia abbreviata*, sclerine stratification. (× 2000).

SACCOLOMA (Fig. 169 A), CYSTODIUM (Fig. 169 B):—

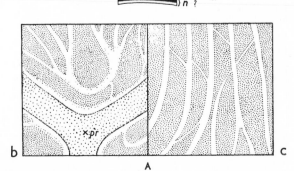

Fig. 169 A. *Saccoloma elegans*; a, sclerine stratification (p, perine?; s, sexine ?; n, nexine ?; × 2000); b, part of proximal face (pr, proximal pole); c, part of distal face (b and c × 4250).

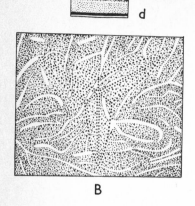

d

B

Fig. 169 B. *Cystodium sorbifolium*, part of distal face (× 1000); d, sclerine stratification; the small rounded excrescences of the thin outermost (perinous ?) stratum are cross-sections of the narrow white ridges exhibited in the main figure (× 2000).

SALVINIA:—

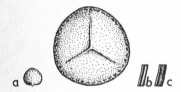

a   b c

Fig. 170. *Salvinia cucullata*, microspore; a, lateral view (× 250); b, exine stratification at the transition between the two faces (× 2000); c, exine stratification, proximal face (× 2000); main figure: proximal face (× 1000).

SCHIZAEA: see Fig. 143 E, F, p. 78.

SELAGINELLA:—

Megaspores: *S. firmula* (Fig. 171), *S. rupestris* (Fig. 172), *S. selaginoides* (Pl. III, facing p. 94; Fig. 173).
Microspores: *S. apus* (Fig. 174), *S. atroviridis* (Fig. 175), *S. biformis* (Fig. 176), *S. eggersii* (Fig. 177), *S. flagellata* (Fig. 178), *S. kraussiana* (Fig. 179), *S. radiata* (Fig. 180), *S. selaginoides* (Fig. 181), *S. uncinata* (Fig. 182).

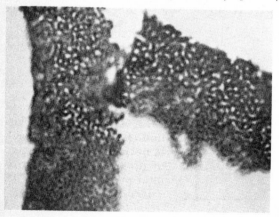

Fig. 171. *Selaginella firmula*. Fragment of section through megaspore membrane. × 2000.

Fig. 172. *Selaginella rupestris*. Fragment of section through megaspore membrane. × 1000.

Fig. 173. *Selaginella selaginoides*. Fragment of section through megaspore membrane (× 2000). An electron micrograph showing the fine structure of part of the membrane is shown in Pl. III (facing p. 94), lower figure.

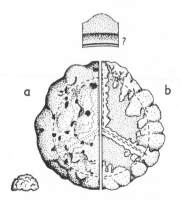

Fig. 174. *Selaginella apus*, microspore. a, distal face; b, proximal face (a, b × 1000). Lower left-hand detail: lateral view (× 250); upper detail: sclerine stratification (× 2000).

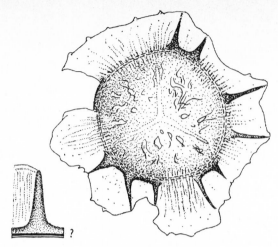

Fig. 175. *Selaginella atroviridis*, microspore; sclerine stratification (× 2000) and distal face (× 1000).

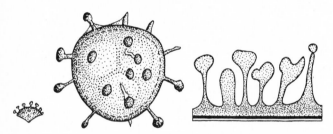

Fig. 176. *Selaginella biformis*, microspore. From left to right: lateral view (× 250); distal face (× 1000); exine stratification (× 2500).

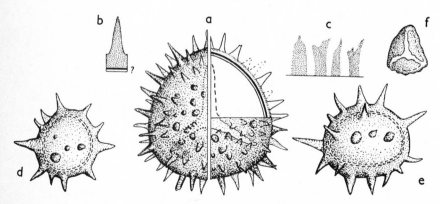

Fig. 177. *Selaginella eggersii*, microspore. a, distal (left) and proximal face (right; surface and section); b, sclerine stratification; c, different types of processes; d–f, aberrant microspores. — a, d–f × 1000; b, c × 2000.

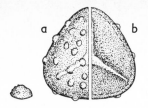

Fig. 178. *Selaginella flagellata*, microspore; lateral view (× 250) and distal (a) and proximal (b) face (× 1000).

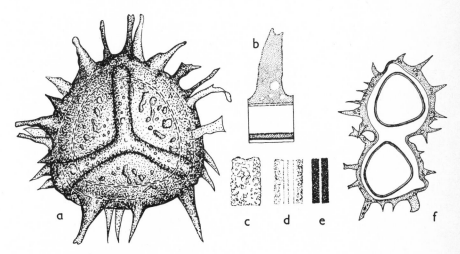

Fig. 179. *Selaginella kraussiana*, microspore; a, proximal face (× 1000); b, sclerine stratification (× 2000); c–e, successive patterns in LO-analysis of the laesura; f, two microspores with common cover (× 1000).

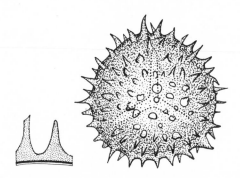

Fig. 180. *Selaginella radiata*, microspore; sclerine stratification (× 2000) and distal face (× 1000).

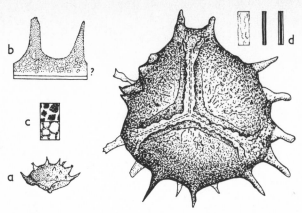

Fig. 181. *Selaginella selaginoides*, microspore. Main figure: proximal face (× 1000). a, lateral view (× 250); b, sclerine stratification (× 2000); c, LO-patterns; d, part of laesura at different adjustments from high (left) to low (right).

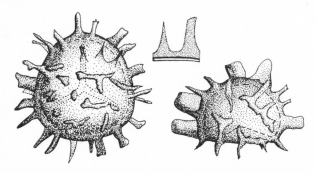

Fig. 182. *Selaginella uncinata*, microspores in polar (left; distal face) and lateral view (right; both × 1000). In the centre: sclerine stratification (× 2000).

SELENODESMIUM: see Fig. 188 A, p. 96.

STENOCHLAENA:—

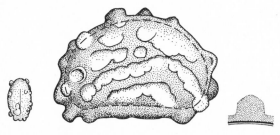

Fig. 183. *Stenochlaena tenuifolia*. From left to right: proximal face (× 250); lateral view (surface and section; × 1000); sclerine stratification (× 2000).

Pl. III.

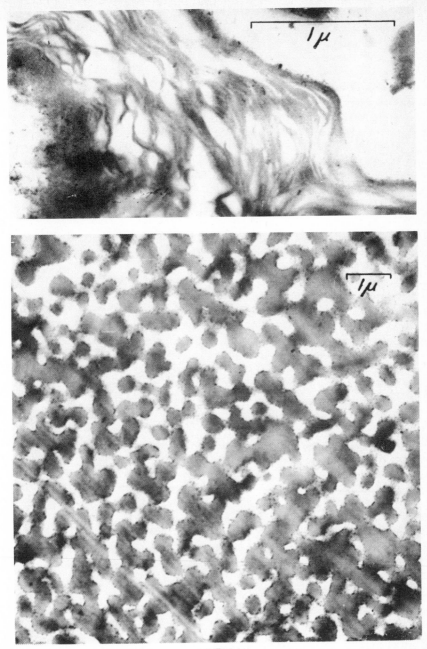

Lycopodium clavatum and *Selaginella selaginoides*. Upper figure: section through the exine in *Lycopodium clavatum*. An outer laminated and an inner granulated layer can be seen. EMG B. M. Afzelius (× 40,000). Lower figure: section through part of the exine of a megaspore of *Selaginella selaginoides*. EMG B. M. Afzelius (× 12,500). (From Svensk bot. Tidskr., vol. 48, 1954.)

STICHERUS: see Fig. 114 B, p. 63.

STROMATOPTERIS: see Fig. 114 A, p. 63.

TAENITIS:—

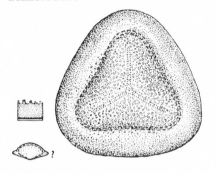

Fig. 184. *Taenitis blechnoides*. From left to right: sclerine stratification (× 2000) and lateral view (× 250); distal face (× 1000); LO-patterns.

TAPEINIDIUM:—

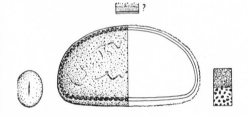

Fig. 185. *Tapeinidium pinnatum*; proximal face (× 250); lateral view (surface and optical cross-section; × 1000); LO-patterns.

THYRSOPTERIS:—

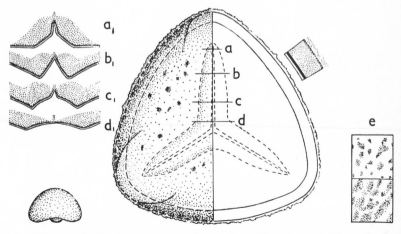

Fig. 186. *Thyrsopteris elegans*; proximal face (surface and optical cross-section; × 1000). Optical cross-sections through the laesura at a–d are shown in a_1–d_1. e, LO-patterns. Lower left-hand detail: lateral view (× 250); upper right-hand detail: sclerine stratification (× 2000).

TMESIPTERIS:—

Fig. 187. *Tmesipteris forsteri*, sclerine stratification (× 2000).

TODEA: see Fig. 155 F, p. 84.

TRICHOMANES (Fig. 188 A, B, D), HYMENOPHYLLUM (Fig. 188 C):—

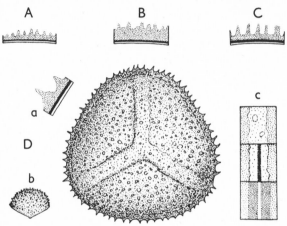

Fig. 188. Hymenophyllaceae. A–C, *Trichomanes* and *Hymenophyllum*, exine stratification (× 2000). A, *T. (Selenodesmium) rigidum*. B, *T. (Macroglena) meifolium*. C, *Hymenophyllum (Hymenoglossum) cruentum*. D, *Trichomanes (Vandenboschia) radicans*, proximal face (× 1000); a, exine stratification (× 2000); b, lateral view (× 250); c, LO-analysis of laesura.

VANDENBOSCHIA: see Fig. 188 D.

VITTARIA:—

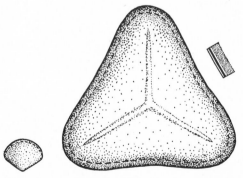

Fig. 189. *Vittaria vittarioides*. From left to right: lateral view (× 250); proximal face (× 1000); sclerine stratification (× 2000).

WOODSIA:—

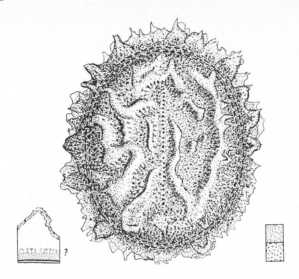

Fig. 190. *Woodsia alpina*. From left to right: sclerine stratification (× 2000); distal face (× 1000); LO-patterns.

XIPHOPTERIS:—

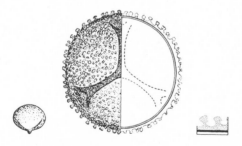

Fig. 191. *Xiphopteris saffordii*. From left to right: lateral view (× 250); proximal face (surface and optical cross-section; × 1000); exine stratification (× 2000).

"... opening several of these dry red Cases, I found them to be quite hollow, without any thing at all in them; whereas when I cut them asunder with a sharp Pen-knife when green, I found in the middle of this great Case, another smaller round Case, between which two, the *interstices* were fill'd with multitudes of stringie *fibres,* which seem'd to suspend the lesser Case in the middle of the other, which (as farr as I was able to discern) seem'd full of exceeding small white seeds ..."

From a description of moss capsules in R. Hooke's Micrographia 1667 (pp. 131, 132).

BRYOPHYTA

Pl. IV (facing p. 108), V (facing p. 109); Figs. 192–253.

HEPATICAE

Aneuraceae: Fig. 240 (p. 118).

Anthocerotaceae: Figs. 194 (p. 100), 208 (p. 106), 225 (p. 112).

Blasiaceae: Fig. 197 (p. 101).

Cleveaceae: Fig. 204 (p. 104).

Codoniaceae: Fig. 213 (p. 108).

Conocephalaceae: Fig. 205 (p. 104).

Corsiniaceae: Fig. 206 (p. 105).

Cyathodiaceae: Fig. 207 (p. 105).

Exormothecaceae: Fig. 211 (p. 108).

Frullaniaceae: Fig. 214 (p. 109).

Grimaldiaceae: Fig. 232 (p. 115).

Marchantiaceae: Fig. 209 (p. 106).

Monocleaceae: Fig. 226 (p. 113).

Oxymitraceae: Fig. 230 (p. 114).

Pelliaceae: Fig. 231 (p. 115).

Plagiochilaceae: Fig. 233 (p. 116).

Radulaceae: Fig. 238 (p. 118).

Ricciaceae: Fig. 241 (p. 119).

Riellaceae: Fig. 242 (p. 120).

Scapaniaceae: Fig. 243 (p. 121).

Sphaerocarpaceae: Fig. 216 (p. 109).

Symphyogynaceae: Fig. 250 (p. 123).

Targioniaceae: Fig. 251 (p. 123).

MUSCI

Andreaeaceae: Fig. 192 (p. 100).

Archidiaceae: Fig. 195 (p. 101).

Bryaceae: Fig. 199 A–C, E (p. 102).

Buxbaumiaceae: Fig. 200 A, B (p. 102).

Calomniaceae: Fig. 201 (p. 103).

Calymperaceae: Fig. 202 (p. 103).

Catascopiaceae: Fig. 224 D (p. 112).

Dicranaceae: Fig. 203 B (p. 103).

Diphysciaceae: Fig. 200 C (p. 102).

Ditrichaceae: Fig. 203 A (p. 103).

Encalyptaceae: Fig. 210 (p. 107).

Ephemeraceae: Fig. 227 (p. 113).

Fissidentaceae: Fig. 212 (p. 107).

Funariaceae: Pl. IV, V.

Georgiaceae: Fig. 215 (p. 109).

Gigaspermaceae: Fig. 217 (p. 110).

Grimmiaceae: Fig. 239 (p. 118).

Hedwigiaceae: Fig. 218 (p. 110).

Helicophyllaceae: Fig. 219 (p. 110).

Hookeriaceae: Fig. 220 (p. 111).

Hylocomiaceae: Fig. 221 (p. 111).

Lembophyllaceae: Fig. 228 A (p. 113).

Leptostomaceae: Fig. 222 (p. 111).

Leskeaceae: Fig. 223 (p. 111).

Leucobryaceae: Fig. 203 C (p. 103).

Meeseaceae: Fig. 224 A–C (p. 112).

Mniaceae: Fig. 199 D (p. 102).

Neckeraceae: Fig. 228 B (p. 113).

Oedipodiaceae: Fig. 229 (p. 114).

Orthotrichaceae: Fig. 253 (p. 124).

Pleurophascaceae: Fig. 234 (p. 116).

Polytrichaceae: Fig. 235 (p. 116).

Pottiaceae: Figs. 193 (p. 100), 236 (p. 117).

Rhizogoniaceae: Fig. 237 (p. 117).

Schistostegaceae: Fig. 244 (p. 121).

Sphagnaceae: Fig. 246 (p. 121).

Spiridentaceae: Fig. 247 (p. 122).

Splachnaceae: Fig. 248 (p. 122).

Symphyodontaceae: Fig. 249 (p. 122).

Timmiaceae: Fig. 252 (p. 124).

ACROSCHISMA:—

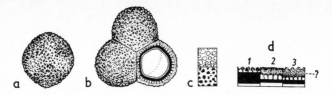

Fig. 192. *Acroschisma wilsonii*; a, distal face (× 1000); b, tetrad (× 1000); c, LO-patterns (distal face); d, exine stratification (1, in chlorinated spores); × 2000.

ANOECTANGIUM:—

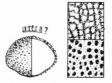

Fig. 193. *Anoectangium aestivum*; spore in lateral view, surface and optical section (distal pole upwards; × 1000); LO-patterns (distal face).

ANTHOCEROS:—

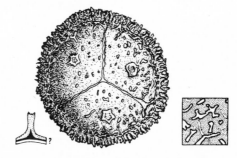

Fig. 194. *Anthoceros tuberculatus*; from left to right: sclerine stratification (× 2000); proximal face (× 825); LO-pattern.

ARCHIDIUM:—

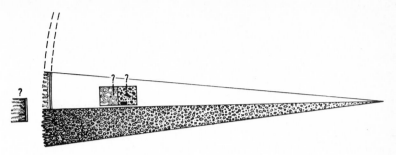

Fig. 195. *Archidium alternifolium*; part of spore surface (× 1000).

ATHALAMIA:—

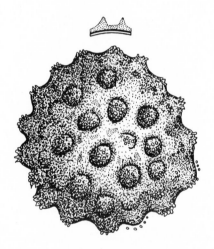

Fig. 196. *Athalamia nana*; spore (× 1000) and sclerine stratification (×2000).

BLASIA:—

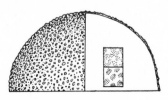

Fig. 197. *Blasia pusilla*; part of spore, surface and optical section (× 1000).

BLINDIA: see Fig. 203 B, p. 103.

BRACHIOLEJEUNIA:—

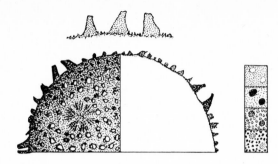

Fig. 198. *Brachiolejeunia sandwicensis*; part of spore, surface and optical section (× 1000); sclerine stratification (× 2000) and LO-patterns.

BRYUM (Fig. 199 A, B), CINCLIDIUM (Fig. 199 E), MIELICHHOFERIA (Fig. 199 E), POHLIA (Fig. 199 C):—

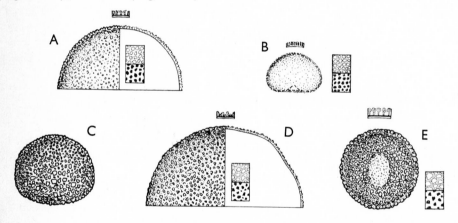

Fig. 199. Bryaceae (A, B, C, E), Mniaceae (D). — A, *Bryum mammillatum*; part of spore, surface and optical section (× 1000). B, *B. caespiticium*; spore in lateral view (× 1000). C, *Pohlia elongata*; spore in lateral view (× 1000). D, *Cinclidium subrotundum*; part of spore, surface and optical section (× 1000). E, *Mielichhoferia elongata*; cf. proximal face (× 1000).

BUXBAUMIA (Fig. 200 A, B), DIPHYSCIUM (Fig. 200 C):—

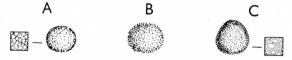

Fig. 200. Buxbaumiales. A, *Buxbaumia aphylla*. B, *B. viridis*. C, *Diphyscium foliosum*. (A–C × 1000).

CALOMNIUM:—

Fig. 201. *Calomnium laetum*; surface and optical section (× 1000), exine stratification (× 2000) and LO-patterns.

CALYMPERES:—

Fig. 202. *Calymperes afzelii*; surface and optical section (× 1000), exine stratification (× 2000) and LO-patterns.

CATASCOPIUM: see Fig. 224 D, p. 112.

CERATODON (Fig. 203 A), BLINDIA (Fig. 203 B), LEUCOBRYUM (Fig. 203 C):—

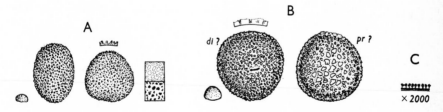

Fig. 203. Dicranales. — A, *Ceratodon purpureus*; from left to right: spore in lateral view (× 250); two spores (cf. proximal face; × 1000); LO-patterns. B, *Blindia acuta*; from left to right: spore in lateral view (× 250); cf. distal face (× 1000); cf. proximal face (× 1000). C, *Leucobryum glaucum*; exine stratification (× 2000).

CINCLIDIUM: see Fig. 199 D, p. 102.

CLEVEA:—

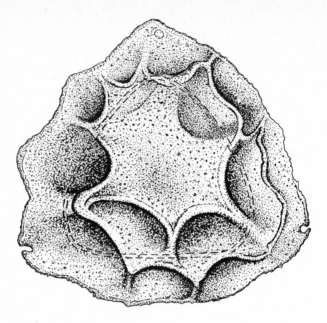

Fig. 204. *Clevea robusta*; distal face (× 1000).

CONOCEPHALUM:—

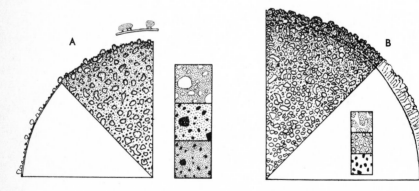

Fig. 205. A, *Conocephalum (Fegatella) conicum*; part of spore (× 1000), optical section and surface; LO-patterns. B, *C. supradecompositum*; part of spore (× 1000), surface and optical section (with LO-patterns).

CORSINIA:—

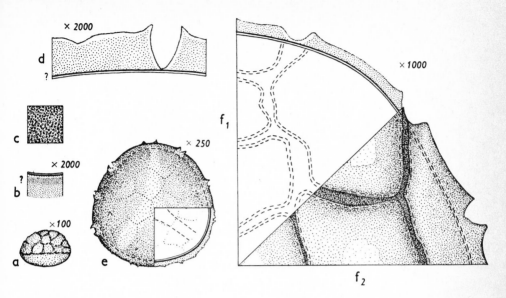

Fig. 206. *Corsinia curiandrina*. a, lateral view; b, sclerine stratification in the less convex face; c, LO-pattern; d, sclerine stratification in the more convex face; e, polar view (less convex face); f₁, f₂: part of spore in polar view (f₁, optical section, f₂, surface).

CYATHODIUM:—

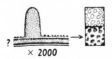

Fig. 207. *Cyathodium africanum*; sclerine stratification and LO-patterns.

DENDROCEROS:—

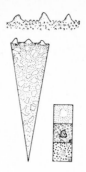

Fig. 208. *Dendroceros crispatus*; part of spore surface (× 1000).

DIPHYSCIUM: see Fig. 200 C, p. 102.

DUMORTIERA:—

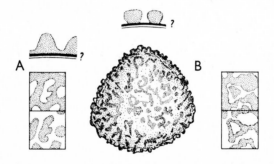

Fig. 209. *Dumortiera hirsuta*; exine stratification (× 2000) and LO-patterns. B, *D. velutina*; spore in polar view (× 1000), exine stratification (× 2000), and LO-patterns.

ENCALYPTA:—

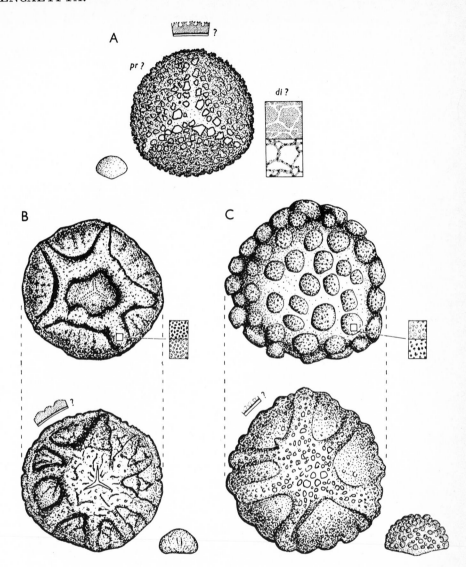

Fig. 210. A, *Encalypta alpina*. From left to right: spore in lateral view (×250); cf. proximal face (× 1000); LO-patterns in the distal (?) face. B, *E. ciliata*; distal face (upper figure) and proximal face (lower figure; both × 1000); the lower right-hand detail shows a spore in lateral view (× 250). C, *E. rhabdocarpa*; distal face (upper figure) and proximal face (lower figure; both × 1000); the lower right-hand detail shows a spore in lateral view (× 250).

108

EXORMOTHECA:—

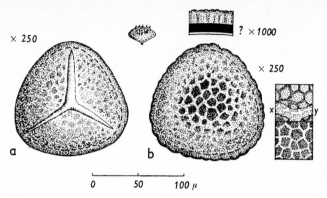

Fig. 211. *Exormotheca fimbriata*; a, proximal, b, distal face (× 250). The LO-patterns to the extreme right exhibit—at x-y—a part of one of the muroid ridges shown in b, and also the "insulous" condition in the bottom of the lumina.

FISSIDENS:—

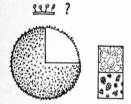

Fig. 212. *Fissidens adiantoides*; surface and optical section (× 1000), exine stratification (× 2000), and LO-patterns.

FOSSOMBRONIA:—

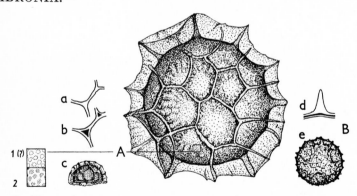

Fig. 213. A, *Fossombronia angulosa*; spore (× 1000); a, part of "muri" at high and, in b, at slightly lower adjustment of the microscope; c, spore, lateral view (× 250); the LO-patterns to the extreme left show the patterns at the bottom of the lumina. B, *F. dumortieri*; d, exine stratification (with "murus", × 2000); e, spore (proximal face ?), × 250.

FRULLANIA:—

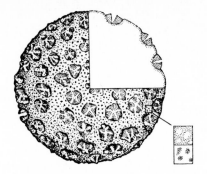

Fig. 214. *Frullania involvens*; surface and optical section (× 1000).

FUNARIA: see Pl. IV, V (facing pp. 108, 109)

GEORGIA:—

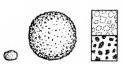

Fig. 215. *Georgia pellucida*; from left to right: spore in lateral view (× 250); spore in polar view (× 1000); LO-patterns.

GEOTHALLUS:—

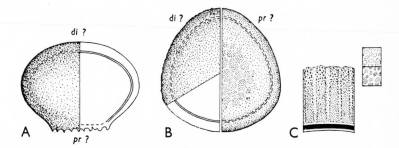

Fig. 216. *Geothallus tuberosus*; A, lateral view (× 250); B, polar view (di = cf. distal face, surface and optical section; pr = cf. proximal face, surface, × 250); C, sclerine stratification (about × 2000).

GIGASPERMUM (Fig. 217 B), LORENTZIELLA (Fig. 217 A):—

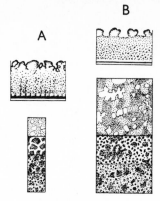

Fig. 217. Gigaspermaceae. — A, *Lorentziella paraguensis*; sclerine stratification ($\times$ 2000) and LO-patterns. B, *Gigaspermum repens*; sclerine stratification ($\times$ 2000) and LO-patterns.

HEDWIGIA (Fig. 218 A), HEDWIGIDIUM (Fig. 218 B):—

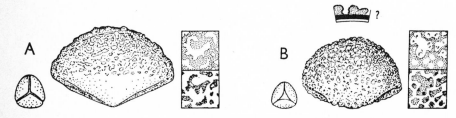

Fig. 218. Hedwigiaceae. — A, *Hedwigia ciliata*; from left to right: proximal face ($\times$ 250); spore in lateral view ($\times$ 1000); LO-patterns. B, *Hedwigidium integrifolium*; from left to right: proximal face ($\times$ 250); spore in lateral view ($\times$ 1000); LO-patterns. (From Erdtman in Svensk bot. Tidskr. 1954.)

HEDWIGIDIUM: see Fig. 218 B.

HELICOPHYLLUM:—

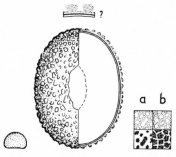

Fig. 219. *Helicophyllum torquatum*; a, LO-patterns, proximal face; b, LO-patterns, distal face; the central figure shows the proximal face of a spore, surface (left) and optical section (right; $\times$ 1000).

HOOKERIA:—

Fig. 220. *Hookeria albicans*; spore (× 1000) and LO-patterns.

HYLOCOMIUM:—

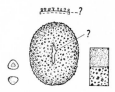

Fig. 221. *Hylocomium splendens*; the main figure shows the supposed proximal spore face (× 1000).

ISOTHECIUM: see Fig. 228 A, p. 113.

LEPTOSTOMUM:

Fig. 222. *Leptostomum macrocarpum*; from left to right: spore in cf. transverse lateral view (× 250); spore in longitudinal lateral view (× 1000); LO-patterns. Upper detail figure: exine stratification (× 2000).

LESKEA:—

Fig. 223. *Leskea polycarpa*; spore, surface and optical section (× 1000). The left part of the right-hand detail figure shows the LO-patterns of the cf. distal face, the right part those of the cf. proximal face.

LEUCOBRYUM: see Fig. 203 C, p. 103.

LORENTZIELLA: see Fig. 217 A, p. 110.

MEESEA (Fig. 224 A, B), CATASCOPIUM (Fig. 224 D), PALUDELLA (Fig. 224 C):—

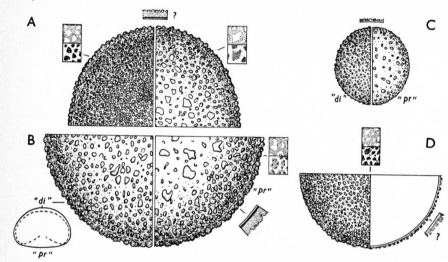

Fig. 224. Meeseaceae (A–C), Catascopiaceae (D). — A, *Meesea longiseta*, cf. distal face (left) and cf. proximal face (right; × 1000). B, *M. uliginosa*, cf. distal face (left) and cf. proximal face (right; × 1000). C, *Paludella squarrosa*, cf. distal face (left) and cf. proximal face (right; × 1000). D, *Catascopium nigritum*, part of spore (× 1000), surface (left) and optical section (right).

MEGACEROS:—

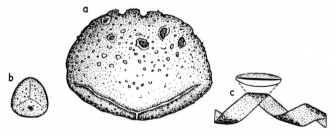

Fig. 225. *Megaceros tosanus*; a, spore in lateral, slightly oblique view (× 1000); b, distal face (× 250); c, elater (× 1000; the detail figure shows the wall stratification, × 2000).

MIELICHHOFERIA: see Fig. 199 E, p. 102.

MONOCLEA:—

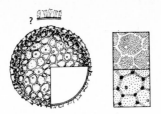

Fig. 226. *Monoclea forsteri*; spore (× 1000), exine stratification (× 2000), and LO-patterns.

NANOMITRIUM:—

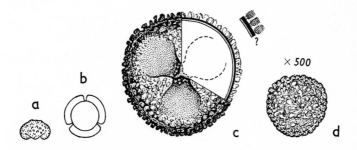

Fig. 227. *Nanomitrium tenerum*; a, lateral view (× 250); b, outline of tetrad (× 250); c, proximal face, surface and optical section (× 1000); d, distal face (× 500).

NECKERA (Fig. 228 B), ISOTHECIUM (Fig. 228 A):—

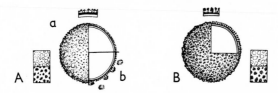

Fig. 228. Neckerinales. — A, *Isothecium myosuroides*; LO-patterns and spore (× 1000); a, surface; b, optical section (upper quadrant without, lower quadrant with, easily detachable "granules"). B, *Neckera complanata*; spore (× 1000), surface and optical section; exine stratification (× 2000), and LO-patterns.

OEDIPODIUM:—

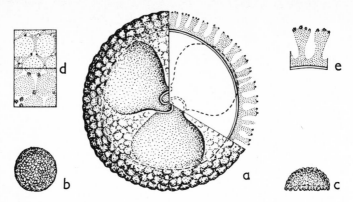

Fig. 229. *Oedipodium griffithianum*; a, proximal face, surface and optical section (× 1000); b, distal face (× 250); c, lateral view (× 250); d, LO-patterns; e, sclerine stratification (about × 2000).

OXYMITRA:—

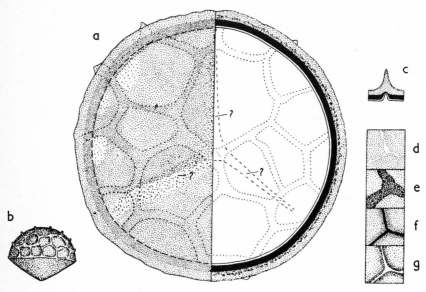

Fig. 230. *Oxymitra paleacea*; a, proximal (?) face, surface (left) and section (right; × 1000); b, spore in lateral view (× 250); c, optical section through a "murus" in the reticulum; d–g, LO-analysis of a "muriferous" part of the spore surface.

PALUDELLA: see Fig. 224 C, p. 112.

PELLIA:—

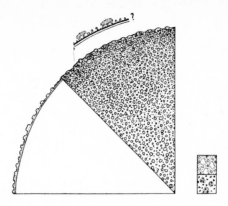

Fig. 231. *Pellia epiphylla*; part of a spore, optical section and surface (×1000); exine stratification (× 2000).

PHASCUM: see Fig. 236 A, p. 117.

PLAGIOCHASMA:—

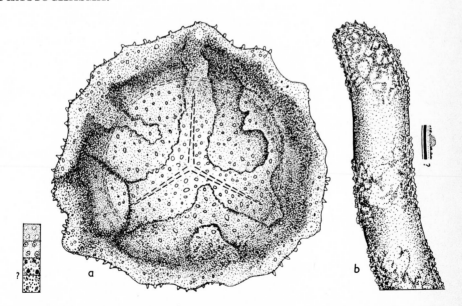

Fig. 232. *Plagiochasma intermedium*; a, proximal face (× 1000) and LO-patterns; b, one half of an elater (× 1000).

PLAGIOCHILA:—

Fig. 233. *Plagiochila asplenioides*; spore (surface and optical section, × 1000); LO-patterns.

PLEUROPHASCUM:—

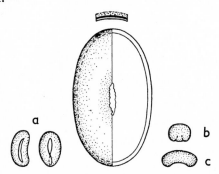

Fig. 234. *Pleurophascum quadrilobum*; main figure: proximal face (surface and optical section; × 1000); a, proximal face (× 250) of slightly irregular spores; b, transverse side view (× 250); c, longitudinal side view (× 250, distal pole upwards).

POHLIA: see Fig. 199 C, p. 102.

POLYTRICHUM:—

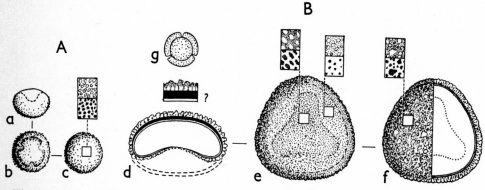

Fig. 235. A, *Polytrichum juniperinum* (× 1000); a, spore in lateral view (proximal pole upwards); b, proximal face; c, distal face and LO-patterns of the square shown in the centre of the face. B, *P. gracile*; d, lateral view; e, proximal (tenuitatiferous) face; f, distal face; g, tetrad (× 250; d–f × 1000).

POTTIA (Fig. 233 B), PHASCUM (Fig. 233 A):—

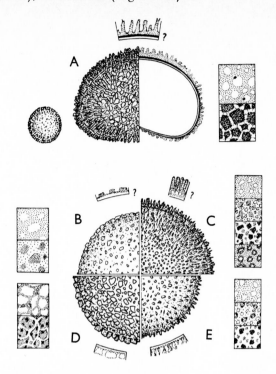

Fig. 236. Pottiaceae (see also Fig. 193, p. 100). — A, *Phascum cuspidatum*, from left to right: spore in polar view (× 250); spore in lateral view, surface (left) and optical section (right; × 1000); LO-patterns. B–E, surface (×1000; only a fourth of a hemisphere shown), sclerine stratification (about × 2000), and LO-patterns in *Pottia crinita* (B), *P. davalliana* (C), *P. truncata* (E), and *P. heimii* (D).

PYRRHOBRYUM:—

Fig. 237. *Pyrrhobryum spiniforme*. From left to right: spore in lateral view (× 250); spore in polar view (× 1000), surface (left) and optical section; LO-patterns.

RADULA:—

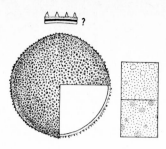

Fig. 238. *Radula lindbergiana*; surface and optical section (lower right-hand quadrant; × 1000); exine stratification (× 2000), and LO-patterns.

RHACOMITRIUM:—

Fig. 239. *Rhacomitrium microcarpon*. From left to right: spore in lateral view (× 250); spore in polar view (× 1000); LO-patterns.

RICCARDIA:—

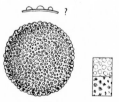

Fig. 240. *Riccardia latifrons*; spore (× 1000); exine stratification (× 2000); LO-patterns.

RICCIA:—

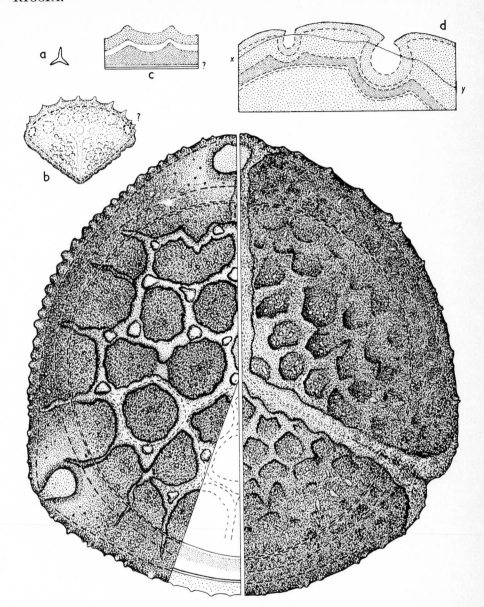

Fig. 241. *Riccia beyrichiana*; main figure: distal face, surface and optical section (left); proximal face, surface (right; × 1000); a, laesura (?); b, spore in lateral view (× 250); c, outline of sclerine stratification (without attempt to classify the layers); d, spore margin (optical section); x–y, approximate limit between distal and proximal face.

RIELLA:—

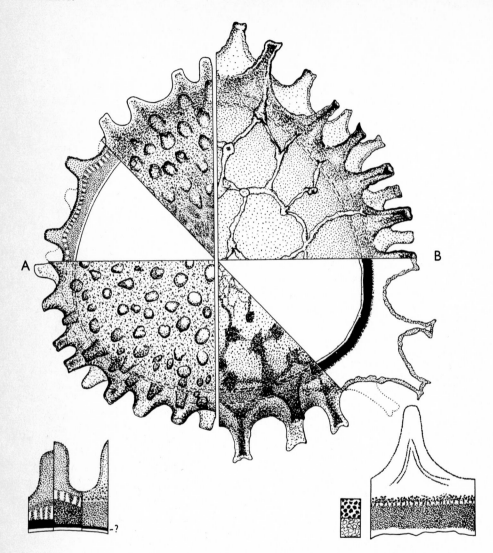

Fig. 242. A, *Riella halophila* (left). B, *R. purpureospora* (right). The sectors in the main figure (A + B) are as follows (enumerated clockwise, beginning at A): sclerine, optical section; part of proximal (?), tenuitatiferous (?) face; part of distal (?) face; sclerine, optical section; part of proximal (?), tenuitati-ferous (?) face; part of distal (?) face. In the lower left-hand detail figure tentative interpretations of the sclerine stratification in *R. halophila* are ex-hibited. The lower right-hand detail shows an outline of the sclerine strati-fication in *R. purpureospora* (the second layer from below should have been blackened in, not dotted); the OL-pattern is due to reticuloid arrangement of the 'sexinous' (cf. endosexinous) elements in the third layer from below.

SCAPANIA:—

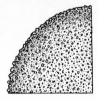

Fig. 243. *Scapania paludicola*; part of spore surface (× 1000); LO-patterns.

SCHISTOSTEGA:—

× 4000 →

Fig. 244. *Schistostega osmundacea*; LO-patterns and five spores (× 1000; from left to right: optical section, distal face of three spores, and spore in lateral view); the upper detail figure exhibiting the exine stratification is enlarged about 4000 times.

SOUTHBYA:—

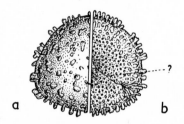

a   b   ?

Fig. 245. *Southbya stillicidiorum*; a, cf. distal face; b, cf. proximal face (× 1000).

SPHAGNUM:—

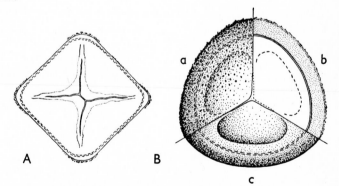

A   B   a   b   c

Fig. 246. A, *Sphagnum fimbriatum*; deviating ("tetrachotomolaesurate" or "4-lete") spore (× 1000). B, *S. palustre*; proximal face of normal (3-lete) spore (× 1000); a, with perine (surface); b, with perine (optical section); c, without perine (surface).

SPIRIDENS:—

Fig. 247. *Spiridens aristifolius;* spore in lateral view (× 1000) ; exine stratification (× 2000).

SPLACHNUM (Fig. 248 C), TAYLORIA (Fig. 248 B), VOITIA (Fig. 248 A).

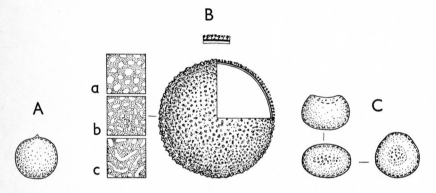

Fig. 248. Splachnaceae. — A, *Voitia nivalis* (× 1000). B, *Tayloria lingulata;*
surface and optical section (× 1000), LO-patterns, and exine stratification
(× 2000). C, *Splachnum vasculosum;* two bilateral spores (the upper in
lateral view, proximal face upwards; the lower in polar view, showing the
cf. proximal tenuitas) and one ± radiosymmetric spore (× 1000).

STROEMIA: see Fig. 253 A, p. 124.

SYMPHYODON:—

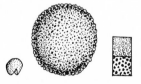

Fig. 249. *Symphyodon echinatus;* spore in lateral (?) view (× 250); spore in
polar (?) view (× 1000); LO-patterns.

SYMPHYOGYNA:—

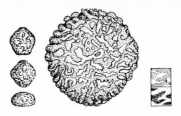

Fig. 250. *Symphyogyna podophylla*; four spores (three × 250, one × 1000); LO-patterns.

TARGIONIA:—

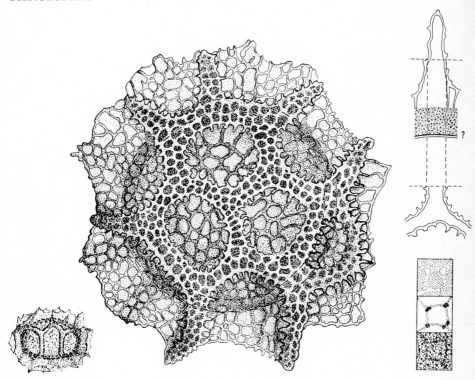

Fig. 251. *Targionia hypophylla*; from left to right: spore in lateral view (× 250); spore in polar view (× 1000); sclerine stratification and LO-patterns.

TAYLORIA: see Fig. 248 B, p. 122.

TIMMIA:—

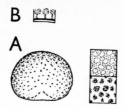

Fig. 252. A, *Timmia austriaca*; spore in lateral view (× 1000); LO-patterns. B, *T. anomala*; exine stratification (× 2000).

ULOTA (Fig. 253 B), STROEMIA (Fig. 253 A):—

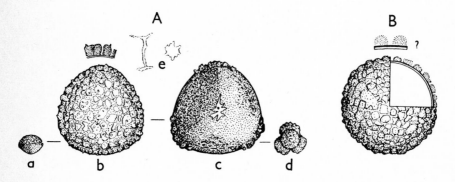

Fig. 253. A, *Stroemia gymnostoma*; a, spore in lateral view (× 250); b, distal face (× 1000); c, proximal face (× 1000); d, tetrad (× 250); e, outline of apertures. B, *Ulota bruchii*; surface and optical section (× 1000).

VOITIA: see Fig. 248 A, p. 122.

INDEX

The references to illustrations are distinguished by heavy figures. Generic names are in italics. The names of species are not included.

126